HARDNESS TESTING

Edited by
Howard E. Boyer

from material compiled by
the ASM Committee on Hardness Testing

ASM INTERNATIONAL
Metals Park, OH 44073

Foreword

This technical manual is a practical handbook dealing with all aspects of hardness testing. Chapter 1 discusses common concepts of hardness, and the theories and methods of hardness testing. Chapters 2 through 5 cover specific hardness testing methods: Brinell, Rockwell, Vickers, and Microhardness testing. Other hardness testing methods, such as Scleroscope, Ultrasonic, Scratch and File testing, and Hardness Evaluation by Eddy Current Testing, are discussed in Chapter 6.

Chapter 7 deals with Hardness Testing Applications: testing of homogeneous and nonhomogeneous materials, ferrous and nonferrous alloys, and nonmetallic materials. Use of hardness testing to measure case depth and evaluate hardenability is also examined.

Chapter 8 looks at the factors that determine the optimum hardness testing method for a specific application: hardness range, nature of the test material, condition of the workpiece, effect of indentation marks, etc. The appendices include metric conversion data, tables for hardness conversions, and industrial directories. The volume is extensively indexed to make it easy to find answers to hardness testing problems.

ASM offers this volume as a guide to those working with hardness testing--from the technician who performs the test to the engineer who evaluates the data. Metallographers, production and quality control personnel should also find it useful.

Preface

There is probably no word in the English language for which so many definitions from so many sources have been offered as the term "hardness." As applied to metals, hardness has always been a subject of much discussion among technical people, resulting in a multiplicity of definitions. Hardness properties include such varied attributes as resistance to abrasives, resistance to plastic deformation, high modulus of elasticity, high yield point, high strength, absence of elastic damping, brittleness, lack of ductility or malleability, high melting temperatures, and magnetic behavior.

Within the scientific community, hardness also represents different concepts. To a metallurgist, it represents resistance to penetration; to a lubrication engineer it means resistance to wear, whereas it denotes a measure of flow stress to a design engineer, resistance to scratching to a mineralogist, and resistance to cutting to a machinist. Although these actions appear to differ greatly in character, they are all related to the plastic flow stress of the material.

Hardness Testing is the result of the efforts of many people to provide current, pertinent information on the subject of testing for hardness. ASM's Editorial Staff wishes to acknowledge Howard Boyer, Nina Farkas, Terri Weintraub, Gerry Rouge, Darlene Vitt and Elaine Wellin for their contributions in the writing, editing and production of this volume. As we move into a new age of engineered materials, the old standby - hardness testing - moves with us. This book is intended to serve as a guide in answering practical questions. We hope you will find it to be a useful reference for many years to come.

ABOUT THE EDITOR

HOWARD E. BOYER began his metallurgical career in 1934 as assistant plant metallurgist for Cooper-Bessemer Corporation, Grove City, PA. From 1939 to 1957 he was Plant Metallurgist for the American Bosch Corporation, Springfield, MA. He was also on the editorial board of **Steel** Publications, having published more than 50 papers and articles, mostly about heat treating. During World War 2 he served as an associate member of the War Production Board.

In 1957 he joined the staff of ASM as Managing Editor of the **Metals Handbook**. In 1973 he became Editor of the **Metals Handbook** and Director of Reference Publications. He officially retired in January 1977, but has continued to work as a technical consultant. Since his retirement he has been an instructor for intensive MEI courses and has prepared MEI lessons. He is the author of **Practical Heat Treating** and co-author of the **Heat Treater's Guide.** He is the editor of the **Atlas of Fatigue Curves** as well as editor of several source books. He was a personal friend of the late Stanley P. Rockwell, and presented the Stanley P. Rockwell Memorial Lecture for the Hartford, CT Chapter of ASM in 1978.

Howard Boyer is a life member of ASM, and a past chairman of the Springfield, MA chapter. He has also been active in SME and ASNT. He resides in Chagrin Falls, OH with his wife Bernice.

CONTENTS

Chapter 1 Introduction to Hardness Testing 1
Approaches to Hardness Testing 1
Common Concepts of Hardness 3
History of Hardness Testing 4
Methods of Hardness Testing 11
Classes of Testing 15

Chapter 2 Brinell Testing 17
Measuring the Indentation 18
Machines for Brinell Testing 22
Precautions and Limitations 28

Chapter 3 Rockwell Hardness Testing 31
Testing Principle 31
Machines for Rockwell Testing 35
Conducting a Rockwell Test 44
Calibration and Maintenance of Rockwell Testers 51

Chapter 4 Vickers Hardness Testing 57
Equipment for Vickers Hardness Testing 58

Chapter 5 Microhardness Testing 67
Knoop and Vickers Microhardness Testing 67
Microhardness Testers 71
Specific Applications of Microhardness Testing 81

Chapter 6 Other Hardness Testing Methods 89
Scleroscope Hardness Testing 89
Test Procedure 94
Ultrasonic Microhardness Testing 97
Capabilities of Ultrasonic Microhardness Testing 102
Limitations of Ultrasonic Hardness Testing 105
Scratch and File Testing 107
Evaluation of Hardness by Eddy Current Testing 109
Electromagnetic Testing 110

Chapter 7 Hardness Testing Applications **115**
    Hardness Testing of Nonhomogeneous Materials 115
    Hardness Testing of Nonferrous Metals 124
    Hardness Testing of Nonmetallic Materials 127
    Hardness Testing of Plastics 127
    Durometer Testing 131
    Special Applications for Hardness Testing 134

Chapter 8 Selection of Hardness Testing Method **141**
    Selection Factors 141

Appendices **149**
    Appendix 1   Hardness Conversion Tables 149
    Appendix 2   Metric and Conversion Data 157
    Appendix 3   Directory of Equipment Manufacturers
                     and Suppliers in the United States 163
    Appendix 4   Directory of Equipment Manufacturers
                     and Suppliers in Canada 171

Chapter 1

Introduction to Hardness Testing

The concept of hardness as it relates to the metals industry can be thought of as resistance to permanent deformation. The scope of hardness properties includes such varied attributes as resistance to abrasives, resistance to plastic deformation, high modulus of elasticity, high yield point, high strength, absence of elastic damping, brittleness, lack of ductility or malleability, high melting temperatures, and magnetic behavior. Within the scientific community, hardness also represents different concepts. To a metallurgist, it represents resistance to penetration; to a lubrication engineer it means resistance to wear, whereas it denotes a measure of flow stress to a design engineer, resistance to scratching to a mineralogist, and resistance to cutting to a machinist. Although these actions appear to differ greatly in character, they are all related to the plastic flow stress of the material.

Approaches to Hardness Testing

The wide variety of tests used to determine hardness may be classified as follows:

- **Static indentation tests,** in which a ball, cone, or pyramid is forced into the surface of the metal being tested. The relationship of load to the area or the depth of indentation is the measure of hardness, such as in the Brinell, Knoop, Rockwell, and Vickers hardness tests.

- **Rebound tests,** in which an object of standard mass and dimensions is bounced from the surface of the workpiece being tested and the height of rebound is the measure of hardness. The Scleroscope is used in rebound tests.

- **Scratch tests,** in which one material is judged as capable of scratching another. The Mohs and file hardness tests are of this type.

- **Plowing tests,** in which a blunt element (usually diamond) is moved across the surface of the workpiece being tested under controlled conditions of load and shape. The width of the groove is the measure of hardness. The Bierbaum test is of this type.

- **Damping tests,** in which the change in amplitude of a pendulum having a hard pivot, which rests on the surface of the workpiece being tested, is the measure of hardness. The Herbert pendulum test is of this type.

- **Cutting tests,** in which a sharp tool of given shape is caused to remove a chip of standard dimensions from the surface of the workpiece being tested.

- **Abrasion tests,** in which a workpiece is loaded against a rotating disk and the rate of wear is the measure of hardness.

- **Erosion tests,** in which sand or other granular abrasive is impinged on the surface of the workpiece being tested under standard conditions and loss of material in a given time is the measure of hardness. Hardness of grinding wheels is measured by this testing method.

- **Electromagnetic testing,** in which hardness is measured as a variable against standards of known flux density.

- **Ultrasonic methods** of evaluating hardness.

In the following chapters, most of the above approaches are covered. However, the discussion concentrates on the methods that are the most widely used--namely, static indentation tests.

Rebound testing is also used extensively, particularly for hardness measurements on large workpieces or for applications in which visible or sharp impressions in the test surface cannot be tolerated.

Common Concepts of Hardness

The hardness test is, by far, the most valuable and most widely used mechanical test for evaluating the properties of metals as well as certain other materials. The hardness of a material usually is considered resistance to permanent indentation. In general, an indenter is pressed into the surface of the metal to be tested under a specific load for a definite time interval, and a measurement is made of the size or depth of the indentation. This book concentrates on static indentation tests for determining the hardness of metals.

The principal purpose of the hardness test is to determine the suitability of a material, or the particular treatment to which the material has been subjected. The ease with which the hardness test can be made has made it the most common method of inspection for metals and alloys.

Why is the hardness test so valuable? Principally, it is because of the relationship that exists between hardness and other properties of material. For example, both the hardness test and the tensile test measure the resistance of a metal to plastic flow. Therefore, the results of these tests may closely parallel each other. The hardness test is preferred, because it is a simple, easy, and relatively nondestructive test.

Hardness is not a fundamental property of a material. Hardness values are arbitrary, and there are no absolute standards of hardness. Hardness has no quantitative value, except in terms of a given load applied in a specified manner for a specified duration and a specified penetrator shape.

Current practice in the United States divides hardness testing into two categories: macrohardness and microhardness. Macrohardness refers to testing with applied loads on the indenter of more than 1 kg and covers, for example, the testing of tools, dies, and sheet material in the heavier gage. On the other hand, microhardness designates testing with applied loads of 1 kg and less on very thin material (down to 0.0125 mm, or 0.0005 in.). This covers extremely small parts, thin superficially hardened parts, plated surfaces, and individual constituents of materials.

History of Hardness Testing

Earlier methods of testing hardness generally consisted of scratching. Because scratch hardness testing, as considered in this book, consists of penetration of the material surface by a testing point, it bears a close resemblance to the indentation hardness test. One of the earliest forms of scratch testing goes back to Reaumur in 1722. His scale of testing consisted of a scratching bar, which increased in hardness from one end to the other. The degree of hardness was determined by the position on the bar that the metal being tested would scratch. In 1822, the Mohs scale of hardness was introduced for minerals and measures the relative hardness of ten minerals. For more information, see Chapter 5.

Other scratch-hardness testers are available that have been used to at least some extent in the metalworking industry, although primarily on a laboratory basis. One of the better known is the Spencer Bierbaum instrument. The principle involved in this test method consists of mechanically drawing the specimen under the diamond, which is lubricated by a fine watch oil during the scratching operation. After the scratch is made, the sample is cleaned of oil. The width of the scratch is read in microns by means of a filar micrometer eyepiece. The scale is derived by using the reciprocal of the cut width in microns squared, multiplied by 10,000:

$$K = 10,000 \ / \ W^2$$

where K is the microcharacter scale, and W is the width of cut in microns.

In the late 19th century, more attention was paid to hardness and its measurement. Brinell, a Swedish engineer, presented a paper to the Swedish Society of Technologists describing his "ball" test. This rapidly became known as the Brinell Test and became universally used in the metalworking industry. Currently, many machines have been devised for making these tests more rapidly and accurately, but the principle has remained essentially unchanged.

Because of the limitations imposed by the Brinell method and increased engineering requirements, several investigators intensified their efforts toward devising other indenters -- principally those made from diamond to accommodate the testing of fully hardened steels. In 1919, the Rockwell test was introduced. It has become, by far, the most popular hardness test in use today, mainly because it overcomes the limitations of the Brinell test.

Theory of Hardness Testing. The hardness values obtained by static indentation tests may be expressed as $C \times Y$, where C is the constraint factor for the test and Y is the uniaxial flow stress of the material being tested. The value of the constraint factor depends mainly on the shape of the indenter used in the hardness test. For many of the common indenters--Brinell, Vickers and Knoop, which are all relatively blunt--the constraint factor is approximately 3.

Fig. 1 Slip-line-field solutions for a flat-ended two-dimensional punch having a width of 2a

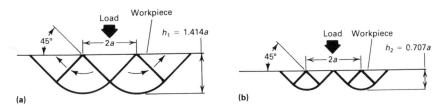

(a)   (b)

(a) Prandtl's flow pattern. Flow in unshaded area is downward and to left and right, as indicated by arrows in shaded areas. (b) Hill's flow pattern. Flow is to left and right in directions indicated by arrows in (a), but is separated
Source: Metals Handbook, Mechanical Testing, Vol. 8, 9th ed., ASM, 1985, p. 72

Prandtl first explained the origin of the constraint factor, C. He likened the blunt hardness indenters used in engineering to a flat-ended punch and proceeded to calculate the mean stress on a two-dimensional punch--that is, one having height and width but no appreciable thickness--for the onset of plastic flow beneath the punch. He assumed a flow pattern beneath the punch that satisfied kinematics. The material within the pattern was assumed to flow plastically in plane strain, and the material surrounding the flow pattern was considered to be rigid. The flow pattern determined by Prandtl, which is shown in Fig. 1(a), predicts a constraint factor C of

$$\left(1 - \frac{\pi}{2}\right).$$

Hill generalized Prandtl's approach into what is now known as the slip-line-field theory. Conditions of equilibrium need not be satisfied in the slip-line-field approach, and hence a unique solution is not obtained. For each kinematically admissible flow pattern, an upper-bound solution is obtained. Hill proposed the slip-line-field solution shown in Fig. 1(b), which leads to the same value of C as the pattern determined by Prandtl (that is, $C = 2.57$). According to these theories, the material displaced by the punch is accounted for by upward flow. Constraint factor C may be termed a "flow constraint" from the slip-line-field point of view.

Fig. 2 Slip-line-field solution for a flat-ended circular punch as determined by Shield

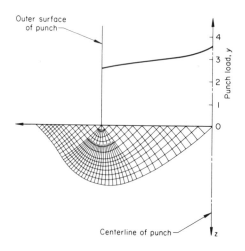

Source: Metals Handbook, Nondestructive Inspection and Quality Control, Vol. 11, 8th ed., ASM, 1976, p. 2

The calculated value of 2.57 is reasonably close to the observed value of 3, particularly considering that the calculation is for a two-dimensional punch, whereas the actual indenter is three-dimensional. Shield extended the plane-strain slip-line-field solution of Hill to a flat-ended circular punch (Fig. 2). In this instance, the pressure on the punch, and on the material beneath the punch, is not uniform, but decreases near the outer surface of the punch where constraint is less. The value of *C* in this instance was calculated to be 2.82--even closer to 3 than for the two-dimensional punches.

Because of the reasonably close agreement between the observed and calculated integrated force on a hardness indenter, the slip-line-field explanation for *C* has been widely accepted. However, when a large block of material having a grid applied to a central vertical plane is loaded by a spherical indenter, flow patterns such as those shown in Fig. 3(a) and (b) are obtained. These flow patterns bear little resemblance to those determined by Hill and Shield. The extent of the region of fully developed plastic flow may be determined precisely by sighting along the deformed grid lines and observing the area as outlined by the circular line in Fig. 3(b). This line separates the elastic region (outside the line) from the fully plastic region (inside the line).

Fig. 3 Deformed grid pattern on a meridianal plane in a Brinell hardness test

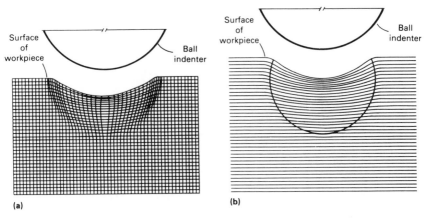

(a) Modeling clay. (b) Low-carbon steel
*Source: **Metals Handbook, Mechanical Testing**, Vol. 8, 9th ed., ASME, 1985, p. 72*

The circular line in Fig. 3(b) resembles one of the lines of constant maximum shear stress for the elastic solution determined by Hertz for a rigid spherical indenter of very large radius that is pressed against an elastic, semi-infinite body. Figure 4 shows the spherical interface between the indenter and the body as a flat surface, and the values of M' on the lines of constant maximum shear stress are equal to the ratio of the maximum shear stress in the body to the mean stress (unit load) on the indenter.

The elastic-plastic boundary in Fig. 3(b) is found to correspond closely to the dashed line of Fig. 4, for which $M' = 0.18$. If the maximum shear stress on this line is assumed to equal $(Y/2)$ by the maximum-shear theory, then the mean stress on the indenter will be $(Y/2)$ $(M') = 2.8$. This corresponds to a constraint factor C of 2.8, which agrees with the results of Shield.

Fig. 4 Hertz lines of constant maximum shear stress on a meridianal plane below the surface of an elastic, semi-infinite body, caused by a frictionless load from a rigid sphere of very large radius

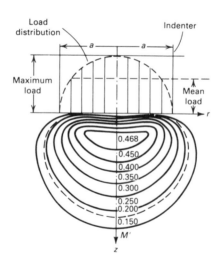

M' = *maximum shear stress in body divided by mean stress (unit load) on the sphere*
Source: **Metals Handbook, Mechanical Testing**, Vol. 8, 9th ed., ASM, 1985, p. 72

Shaw and DeSalvo have shown that if the test piece (workpiece) extends at least $10d$ (where d is the diameter of the indentation) in all directions from the indenter, the displaced volume may be accounted for by the elastic decrease in volume. Therefore, there is no need for upward flow and the elastic theory is in complete agreement with Fig. 3. The constraint factor that arises in this way is termed an elastic-constraint factor, because the displaced volume is accommodated by an elastic decrease in volume instead of by upward flow, as in the slip-line-field approach.

Fig. 5 Grid patterns on transverse planes of modeling-clay specimens in plane strain by a flat punch

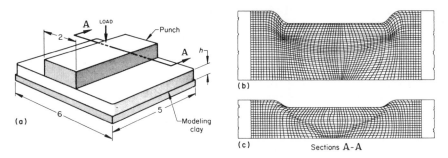

(a) Arrangement for the test. (b) Pattern obtained when h = 1.414a as in Fig.1(a). (c) Pattern obtained when h = 0.707a as in Fig.1(b). Test specimens of both thicknesses were supported by a rigid steel plate
*Source: **Metals Handbook, Nondestructive Inspection and Quality Control**, Vol. 11, 8th ed., ASM, 1976, p. 3*

The basic difference between the slip-line-field and elastic theories of hardness lies in the assumption regarding the behavior of the material that surrounds the plastic zone. The slip-line-field theory assumes this material to be rigid, whereas the elastic theory assumes it to be elastic. As shown in Fig. 3, the flow pattern for a blunt indenter operating on a semi-infinite body does not correspond to that derived using the plastic-rigid theory (Fig. 1). However, experiments with blunt punches may be devised that do produce the flow patterns of Prandtl and Hill shown in Fig. 1(a) and (b). By placing a layer of modeling clay of thickness $h = 1.414a$ (where a is the half-width of the punch) on a steel substrate (Fig. 5a), the plastic-rigid theory is justified (see Fig. 1a). As Fig. 5(b) shows, a flow pattern that resembles the Prandtl slip-line-field solution is obtained. Similarly, when a thinner layer of modeling clay, $h = 0.707a$ (Fig. 1b), is placed on the rigid steel substrate, the flat punch produces a flow pattern (Fig. 5c) that closely resembles that in Fig. 1(b).

Figure 3 directly supports the elastic theory of hardness for a blunt indenter. Further support is the fact that shot peening produces residual compressible stresses that are of importance to fatigue life. Although these compressible stresses are consistent with the elastic theory, they are not included in the slip-line-field theory.

According to the elastic theory, when a blunt indenter is pressed into a plane surface, material beneath the indenter deforms plastically without upward flow, and the elastic stress field is the same as though there were no plastic flow. When the load is removed, there is "plastic recovery"--that is, plastic deformation in a direction opposite to the initial flow but over a smaller volume. Because plastic recovery is not complete, biaxial residual compressible stresses remain in planes parallel to the free surface after the load is removed.

Fig. 6 Slip-line-field solution for two-dimensional indentation

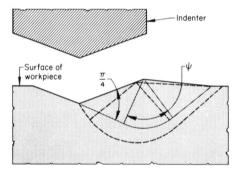

Solid lines correspond to the frictionless case, where $\psi = 70$; dashed lines correspond to the case with friction. The pattern for a frictionless indenter acting on annealed material will also resemble the dashed line pattern
*Source: **Metals Handbook, Nondestructive Inspection and Quality Control**, Vol. 11, 8th ed., ASM, 1976, p. 3*

The elastic theory suggests that strain-hardening tendency and friction on the indenter surface should not influence constraint factor *C*. Alternatively, the slip-line-field theory suggests that increased friction on an indenter will cause an increase in constraint factor *C*. The solid lines of Fig. 6

correspond to the slip-line-field solution for a Vickers indenter with zero friction, and the dashed lines are for a case with friction. The constraint factor C in both instances will be $1 + \psi$, and C will obviously be greater with friction. A similar shift in the slip-line pattern takes place when the work metal tends to work harden. Therefore, the slip-line-field theory suggests that an increase in the constraint factor C occurs with a tendency toward work hardening and with increased friction.

Methods of Hardness Testing

Hardness is evaluated by the amount of permanent deformation or plastic flow of the material. This amount of flow may be determined by measuring the depth of the indentation, or by measuring the area. As the test material becomes softer, the depth of penetration becomes greater. Likewise, the projected area increases as the test material becomes softer. By one of the most common methods of hardness testing--the Rockwell test--hardness is determined by the depth of the indentation in the test material resulting from application of a given force on a specific indenter.

By another widely used method of hardness testing--the Brinell--hardness is evaluated by the area of the impression created by forcing a specific indenter into the test material under a specific force for a given length of time. However, in highly automated Brinell testing systems, hardness is evaluated by depth of the impression, which makes it similar to the Rockwell test in basic principle.

Reversing the Principle of Indentation Testing. Certain modifications of these approaches to indentation testing have been tried, and some have achieved a degree of commercial importance. Probably the most notable attempt was the Monotron tester. This instrument used a 0.75-mm (0.03-in.) hemispherical diamond indenter. The Monotron principle was the reverse of the more conventional indentation testers such as the Brinell and Rockwell. Instead of using a prescribed force and measuring the depth or area, the Monotron indenter was forced into the material being tested to a given depth, and then the hardness was determined by the force required to achieve this depth of penetration. This instrument was developed primarily for evaluating the true hardness of nitrided cases, which were, at one time, difficult to evaluate accurately.

The Monotron did have certain advantages, although its limitations, together with developments in other hardness testing systems, were apparently responsible for it going "by the board." The Monotron has not been manufactured for many years, and it is doubtful whether any are still in use.

Use of the Rebound Principle. The Scleroscope is the only hardness testing instrument that uses the rebound, or impact resiliency, test to evaluate hardness. The test relates more closely to the elastic limit of the material than to the work-hardening and tensile strength characteristics of indentation tests. It is essentially a dynamic indentation test, in which a diamond-tipped hammer (referred to as a "tup") is dropped from a fixed height onto the surface of the work material. The height of the hammer rebound is a measure of the material hardness.

Microhardness Testing. As stated earlier, "microhardness" indicates that the applied load on the indenter is no greater than 1 kg. As a rule, microhardness is evaluated by measuring the area of the indentation rather than the depth. This subject is discussed in Chapter 5.

Scratch Hardness Testing. At least two instruments have been designed in the United States for quantitatively measuring hardness by the scratch method. The earlier and less familiar one was designed by Professor Graton of Harvard. One instrument, built at the Geophysical Laboratory, was intended to overcome the disadvantages of the Mohs scale by eliminating the personal judgment factor. Also, the overlapping of the hardness ranges of various minerals would be greatly reduced. The instrument consisted primarily of a microscope, stage, sliding weight to apply loads to 3 g, and a diamond point. The diamond was ground to a semicircle, blade-like edge with a 45° included angle. In operation, the mineral being tested is scratched by the diamond, and the scratch is compared with standard limit scratches in the microscope eyepiece. Another form of scratch-hardness testing is that of testing with a file. Both of the above methods are covered in Chapter 6.

Abrasion and Erosion Testing. Because hardness is commonly associated with wear or resistance to wear, one is often used to evaluate the other. However, tests involving abrasion and/or erosion are not made instantly as are indentation hardness tests. Selection of materials for specific applications is often done on the basis of wear resistance, which is directly related to hardness. Therefore, abrasion testing of some type is often used.

Wear rates are most commonly evaluated to improve the service life of parts that ordinarily fail by wear. Wear testing may be required to evaluate whether or not the observed wear rate is normal for the application.

Wear tests generally are less accurate and less reliable than tests of other engineering properties of materials or components. Because there is no universal wear test, wear rates are evaluated by many different procedures. Each is designed to evaluate a specific type or mechanism of wear. A wear test is not a good engineering evaluation unless it is:

- Reliable, that is, capable of producing wear of a certain material in a predictable and statistically significant manner

- Able to rank materials, that is, able to achieve statistically significant differences in wear rates among different types of materials

- Valid, that is, capable of accurately predicting the service performance of a given material

Wear rates can be assessed by either service testing or laboratory testing in a controlled or artificial environment. Few service tests can meet the necessary criteria of reliability and ranking ability; thus, field tests seldom justify confidence. However, laboratory tests usually are conducted under artificial conditions that differ significantly from actual service conditions and thus may be of questionable validity.

Laboratory wear tests usually are conducted using an abrasive. They cannot be considered as more than preliminary screening evaluations and can be misleading when used for material selection, unless they accurately simulate:

- Hardness and particle size of the specific abrasive in the environment that controls wear in service (generally this is the hardest substance in an abrasive mixture)

- Forces causing contact between the abrasive particles and the wear surface (contact pressure)

- Relative motion (both speed and direction) between the abrasive and the wear surface

Two abrasive-wear tests--one simulating high-stress grinding abrasion and the other simulating low-stress scratching abrasion--are known to be reliable, able to rank materials, and valid. These two tests are illustrated schematically in Fig. 7 and 8. Because some of the material properties that appear to provide good resistance to abrasive wear also seem to provide good resistance to adhesive wear, abrasive-wear tests sometimes are used to rank materials for adhesive-wear applications. Nevertheless, such tests never truly simulate adhesive or corrosive wear and thus should not be used as the sole criterion for evaluating resistance to these types of wear.

Fig. 7 Schematic illustration of a wet-sand abrasion test

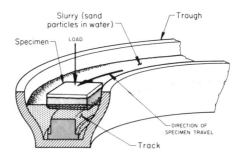

This is a well-validated wear test simulating high-stress grinding abrasion
*Source: **Metals Handbook, Failure Analysis and Prevention**, Vol. 10, 8th ed., ASM, 1975, p. 153*

Service testing represents the ultimate evaluation of wear resistance. Unfortunately, most service situations are subject to great variability. Thus, it may be impossible to find a single material that is best for a given wear application.

Electromagnetic Testing for Hardness. There are innumerable cases in the metalworking industry where one property or function is measured in terms of another. Temperature measurement is a notable example. The thermocouple in a heat treating furnace does not offer a direct measurement of temperature, but instead it registers difference in emf, which is converted to temperature.

Hardness is sometimes evaluated in terms of changes in some other property such as magnetic characteristics.

Fig. 8 Schematic illustration of a dry-sand erosion test used for evaluating resistance to low-stress scratching abrasion

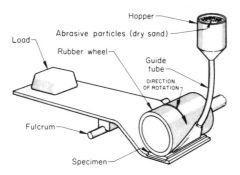

*Source: **Metals Handbook, Failure Analysis and Prevention**, Vol. 10, 8th ed., ASM, 1975, p. 153*

The electromagnetic test is not a hardness test *per se*, but can be used for sorting steel parts on the basis of hardness. Low-frequency comparator-bridge-type instruments are those most commonly used. Sorting is accomplished by use of reference coils that are initially balanced with sample parts of known hardness. Parts of unknown hardness are then substituted for one of the reference parts. The degree of unbalance that results is then correlated with differences in hardness. Additional information on this method, including the equipment and techniques, is presented in Chapter 6.

Classes of Testing

When one views the wide scope of commercial usage to which the hardness test is applied, the test is certainly no less complex than the definition of the term "hardness." There are many means of classifying hardness tests relative to types of machines and materials being tested. The first class incorporates hardness tests that are performed in shops and laboratories (mostly the former) on single parts or representative samples from large lots of parts. Equipment for this type of testing must be accurate and versatile, irrespective of the type of machine or material being tested.

Likewise, it is necessary that such tests are conducted by experienced personnel, or difficulties may result.

The second class of testing includes the type often known as "high-production testing." Modifications of the well-known testing machines have been devised, so that testing can be performed very rapidly, even though the degree of accuracy may be somewhat less. This type of equipment generally is adapted to making many tests on parts of the same physical size and shape. When this condition is changed, it is usually necessary to make a new setup and restandardize the equipment. These machines usually are standardized against similar instruments of the more conventional type.

This classification of hardness testing does not play an important role in manufacturing plants where it is deemed necessary to test all or at least a high percentage of parts. These machines must be regarded as comparators and used with much discretion. The general design of such machines varies over a wide range, starting with large, customized, semiautomatic machines for testing large numbers of similar parts down to and including small portable instruments such as the Brinell hammer, which is used for taking Brinell readings on large castings or other members that are not adaptable to testing by more conventional equipment. This simple instrument must be considered strictly as a comparator.

The third class of hardness testing is performed mainly on a laboratory basis. This does not necessarily mean research laboratories, even though these may be included, but more specifically the testing is performed in process control laboratories. The equipment used for testing may be the same as that used in the first class, although more often such laboratories possess several different hardness testing machines for complete studies. The third class also includes the work performed with the more delicate instruments, especially those used for microhardness testing. These instruments are generally too delicate for shop use, and the parts usually require special preparation.

This type of testing has been received with increasing favor during the past several years. It is partially due to the fast growing field of quality control. Hardness testing is only one phase in the field of inspection where quality control has proved that samples of lots inspected thoroughly are generally more effective as a control method than many tests conducted on a less thorough basis.

Chapter 2

Brinell Testing

The Brinell test is basically simple, but definite procedures must be followed to obtain accurate results. The test consists of applying a constant load (force), usually 500 to 3000 kg, on a 10-mm (0.4-in.) diameter hardened steel, or tungsten carbide, ball to the flat surface of a workpiece (Fig. 1a). The result is a round impression in the workpiece, as shown in Fig. 1(b). A 500-kg load usually is used for testing relatively soft metal, such as copper and aluminum alloys, whereas a 3000-kg load is used for testing harder materials, such as steels and cast irons. After the load is applied for a specified time (usually 10 to 15 s for hard ferrous materials and about 30 s for soft nonferrous materials), the recovered indentation diameter (Fig. 1b) is measured in millimeters. This time period is required to ensure that plastic flow of the work metal has ceased.

Hardness is evaluated by taking the mean diameter of the indentation (two readings at right angles to each other) and calculating the Brinell hardness number (HB) by dividing the applied load by the surface area of the indentation:

$$HB = \frac{L}{\frac{\pi D}{2} \cdot \left(D \cdot \sqrt{D^2 - d^2} \right)}$$

where L is the load in kg; D is the ball diameter in mm; and d is the diameter of the indentation in mm.

Fig. 1 Brinell indentation process

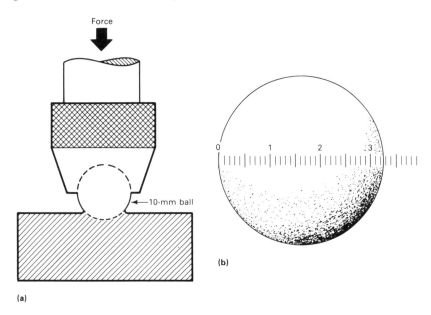

(a) Schematic of the principle of the Brinell indenting process.
(b) Brinell indentation with measuring scale in millimeters
Source: **Metals Handbook, Mechanical Testing**, Vol. 8, 9th ed.,
ASM, 1985, p. 85

It is not necessary to make the above calculation for each test.
Table 1 lists Brinell hardness numbers for indentation
diameters ranging from 2.00 to 6.45 mm (0.078 to 0.25 in.) for
500-, 1000-, 1500-, 2000-, 2500- and 3000-kg loads.

Measuring the Indentation

The indentation diameter is measured to the nearest 0.01
mm (0.0004 in.) with the use of a microscope. The error in
reading the microscope should not exceed 0.01 mm, so that the
error in the Brinell number is less than 1%. A stage
micrometer usually is provided with the microscope and
should be used frequently to check its adjustment.

The Brinell number is based on the surface area of the
indentation. To determine this surface area, it is necessary to

Table 1   Brinell hardness numbers for a 10-mm diameter ball

Dia. of Ball Impression	Brinell Hardness Number For a Load of kg.						Dia. of Ball Impression	Brinell Hardness Number For a Load of kg.					
mm	500	1000	1500	2000	2500	3000	mm	500	1000	1500	2000	2500	3000
2.00	158	316	473	632	788	945	4.25	33.6	67.2	101	134	167	201
2.05	150	300	450	600	750	899	4.30	32.8	65.6	98.3	131	164	197
2.10	143	286	428	572	714	856	4.35	32.0	64.0	95.9	128	160	192
2.15	136	272	408	544	681	817	4.40	31.2	62.4	93.6	125	156	187
2.20	130	260	390	520	650	780	4.45	30.5	61.0	91.4	122	153	183
2.25	124	248	372	496	621	745	4.50	29.8	59.6	89.3	119	149	179
2.30	119	238	356	476	593	712	4.55	29.1	58.2	87.2	116	145	174
2.35	114	228	341	456	568	682	4.60	28.4	56.8	85.2	114	142	170
2.40	109	218–	327	436	545	653	4.65	27.8	55.6	83.3	111	139	167
2.45	104	208	313	416	522	627	4.70	27.1	54.2	81.4	108	136	163
2.50	100	200	301	400	500	601	4.75	26.5	53.0	79.6	106	133	159
2.55	96.3	193	289	385	482	578	4.80	25.9	51.8	77.8	104	130	156
2.60	92.6	185	278	370	462	555	4.85	25.4	50.8	76.1	102	127	152
2.65	89.0	178	267	356	445	534	4.90	24.8	49.6	74.4	99.2	124	149
2.70	85.7	171	257	343	429	514	4.95	24.3	48.6	72.8	97.2	122	146
2.75	82.6	165	248	330	413	495	5.00	23.8	47.6	71.3	95.2	119	143
2.80	79.6	159	239	318	398	477	5.05	23.3	46.6	69.8	93.2	117	140
2.85	76.8	154	230	307	384	461	5.10	22.8	45.6	68.3	91.2	114	137
2.90	74.1	148	222	296	371	444	5.15	22.3	44.6	66.9	89.2	112	134
2.95	71.5	143	215	286	358	429	5.20	21.8	43.6	65.5	87.2	109	131
3.00	69.1	138	207	276	346	415	5.25	21.4	42.8	64.1	85.6	107	128
3.05	66.8	134	200	267	334	401	5.30	20.9	41.8	62.8	83.6	105	126
3.10	64.6	129	194	258	324	388	5.35	20.5	41.0	61.5	82.0	103	123
3.15	62.5	125	188	250	313	375	5.40	20.1	40.2	60.3	80.4	101	121
3.20	60.5	121	182	242	303	363	5.45	19.7	39.4	59.1	78.8	98.5	118
3.25	58.6	117	176	234	293	352	5.50	19.3	38.6	57.9	77.2	96.5	116
3.30	56.8	114	170	227	284	341	5.55	18.9	37.8	56.8	75.6	95.0	114
3.35	55.1	110	165	220	276	331	5.60	18.6	37.2	55.7	74.4	92.5	111
3.40	53.4	107	160	214	267	321	5.65	18.2	36.4	54.6	72.8	90.8	109
3.45	51.8	104	156	207	259	311	5.70	17.8	35.6	53.5	71.2	89.2	107
3.50	50.3	101	151	201	252	302	5.75	17.5	35.0	52.5	70.0	87.5	105
3.55	48.9	97.8	147	196	244	293	5.80	17.2	34.4	51.5	68.8	85.8	103
3.60	47.5	95.0	142	190	238	285	5.85	16.8	33.6	50.5	67.2	84.2	101
3.65	46.1	92.2	138	184	231	277	5.90	16.5	33.0	49.6	66.0	82.5	99.2
3.70	44.9	89.8	135	180	225	269	5.95	16.2	32.4	48.7	64.8	81.2	97.3
3.75	43.6	87.2	131	174	218	262	6.00	15.9	31.8	47.7	63.6	79.5	95.5
3.80	42.4	84.8	127	170	212	255	6.05	15.6	31.2	46.8	62.4	78.0	93.7
3.85	41.3	82.6	124	165	207	248	6.10	15.3	30.6	46.0	61.2	76.7	92.0
3.90	40.2	80.4	121	161	201	241	6.15	15.1	30.2	45.2	60.4	75.3	90.3
3.95	39.1	78.2	117	156	196	235	6.20	14.8	29.6	44.3	59.2	73.8	88.7
4.00	38.1	76.2	114	152	191	229	6.25	14.5	29.0	43.5	58.0	72.6	87.1
4.05	37.1	74.2	111	148	186	223	6.30	14.2	28.4	42.7	56.8	71.3	85.5
4.10	36.2	72.4	109	145	181	217	6.35	14.0	28.0	42.0	56.0	70.0	84.0
4.15	35.3	70.6	106	141	177	212	6.40	13.7	27.4	41.2	54.8	68.8	82.5
4.20	34.4	68.8	103	138	172	207	6.45	13.5	27.0	40.5	54.0	67.5	81.0

Source: MEI Course 12, Mechanical Testing of Metals," Lesson 3, "Hardness Testing," ASM, 1983, p. 6

measure the diameter of the indentation, assuming that this is the diameter of the indentation with which the ball was in actual contact. If it is not, "ridging" and "sinking" impressions may be the cause. In the case of ridging-type impressions, the diameter of the indentation is greater than the true value, whereas with the sinking-type impressions, the reverse is true. Therefore, it cannot be ascertained that the correct diameter has been measured. Consequently, much is left to the judgment and experience of the operator.

In some materials, the brink of the indentation is poorly defined, especially when hardened steels (even with polished surfaces) are tested. The use of cemented tungsten balls produces a more distinct indentation.

In the Brinell test, the indentation may exhibit different surface characteristics, which have been carefully studied and analyzed. When some metals are tested, there is a ridge around the impression extending above the original surface of the test piece (Fig. 2a); at other times, the edge of the impression is below the original surface (Fig. 2b). In some cases, there is no difference (Fig. 2c). The first phenomenon is called a ridging-type impression and the second a sinking-type. Cold worked alloys generally exhibit the former, and annealed metals exhibit the latter.

Fig. 2 Sectional views of Brinell indentations

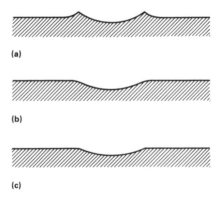

(a)

(b)

(c)

(a) Ridging-type Brinell impression. (b) Sinking-type Brinell impression. (c) Flat-type Brinell impression
*Source: **Metals Handbook, Mechanical Testing**, Vol. 8, 9th ed., ASM, 1985, p. 85*

Brinell indentations made on some materials are not perfectly round. Indentations on materials that have been subjected to considerable rolling are elliptical in shape, whereas those on heat treated steels are quite round. For indentations that are not circular, an average value of the Brinell number may be obtained by measuring the diameter in four directions at approximately 45° apart.

Spacing of Indentations. For accurate results, the indentations must not be made close to the edge of the workpiece. Lack of sufficient supporting material on one side will produce abnormally large and unsymmetrical indentations. Frequently, the error in Brinell number will be negligible if the distance from the center of the indentation is not less than three times the diameter of the indentation from any edge of the workpiece being tested.

Brinell indentations also must not be made too close to one another. When indentations are too close to each other, the material may be cold worked by the first indentation, or there may not be sufficient supporting material for the second indentation. The former condition is likely to produce an abnormally small indentation, whereas the latter condition will result in too large an indentation. The distance between centers of adjacent indentations should be at least three times the diameter of the indentation, so that the error in the Brinell number is 1% or less.

Practical Limits of Hardness Measurement by the Brinell Method. Highly hardened steel (or other extremely hard materials) cannot be tested by a hardened steel ball, because the ball will flatten and become permanently deformed. An appreciable error in the Brinell number occurs when the indentation diameter is less than about 2.90 mm (0.114 in.) (shown as 444 HB in Table 1), when hardened steel balls are used. A special hardened and burnished steel ball called the "Hulked" ball may be used up to 500 HB. Tungsten carbide ball indenters are recommended for hardnesses of 444 to 627 HB (2.90 to 2.45 mm, or 0.11 to 0.10 in., indentations). However, slightly higher hardness values will result when using carbide balls as opposed to steel balls, because of the difference in elastic properties between these materials. ASTM E10 specifies the 10-mm (0.4-in.) ball indenter shall not deviate more than 0.005 mm (0.0002 in.) in any diameter and have a Diamond Pyramid hardness of at least 850 HV. When the material being tested is too soft, inaccuracies occur at an indentation diameter greater than 6 mm (0.25 in.).

Effect of Surface Conditions. The degree of accuracy of the Brinell test is influenced by the surface smoothness (or roughness) of the material being tested. The surface of the workpiece should be filed, ground, or polished, such as with a 3/0 emery paper, so that the indentation is clearly defined to permit accurate measurement. For accurate results, the surface must be representative of the material. Surface decarburization or retained austenite cause erroneous readings on the low side, whereas carburization or any other form of superficial hardening will result in erroneous readings on the high side.

Machines for Brinell Testing

Different types of Brinell testing machines are available. It is essential that the load is not applied too rapidly, because this may result in overloading, thus causing increases in the sizes of the indentations and false readings. The machine, regardless of type, should be capable of applying a uniform load at a rate not exceeding about 500 kg/s. Under this condition, no appreciable error will result from plastic flow of the test material. The machine should be equipped with a pressure or load gage to help the operator keep the load and rate of loading under control.

One of the oldest and most commonly used testing machines is the hydraulic, manually operated type illustrated in Fig. 3. The workpiece is placed on the anvil and brought into contact with the indenter by means of an adjusting screw. Then the force is applied by a manually operated, hydraulic pump until the desired pressure registers on the gage. The pressure is held for the required length of time and released. The workpiece is withdrawn, and the indentation is measured with a 20x power microscope. Testing with this type of apparatus (Fig. 3) is relatively slow and tedious. To complete a single test takes 1 min. A new type of tester uses the proving ring principle to measure the load as applied through a worm gear.

Machines for Production Testing. One type of Brinell testing machine, which greatly speeds up testing and eliminates operator variables without sacrifice to accuracy, is the semiautomatic air-operated machine shown in Fig. 4. A completely automatic hardness testing system is shown in Fig. 5. This system is designed for a production line applications. It is equipped with a digital readout of Brinell hardness numbers, as well as the reading for the depth of penetration

Fig. 3 Conventional hydraulically-operated Brinell hardness tester

Source: MEI Course 12, "Mechanical Testing of Metals," Lesson 3, "Hardness Testing," ASM, 1983, p. 7

and the width of impression. This machine is capable of testing as many as 1200 parts/h. It can be equipped with a sorting device for tolerance limit sorting, and a printout of data can be obtained. Direct reading machines are calibrated to use the depth of impression, which can be obtained by mechanical means, to determine the relative hardness number. Although Brinell hardness is generally recorded as a two- or three-digit number, Brinell is a stress value, given in kilograms per square millimeter, and is an important mechanical property of metals and alloys.

Fig. 4 Semiautomatic air-operated Brinell hardness tester

This tester is faster and better adapted to production testing than is the manually operated type shown in Fig. 3
Source: *MEI Course 12, "Mechanical Testing of Metals," Lesson 3, "Hardness Testing," ASM, 1983, p. 7*

Portable Machines for Brinell Testing. The use of conventional hardness testers occasionally may be limited because: (1) the work must be brought to the machine, and (2) despite the adjustable throats, which are available on stationary machines, the workpieces must be able to be placed between the anvil and the indenter. Portable Brinell testers

Fig. 5 Automatic Brinell hardness testing system with digital readout

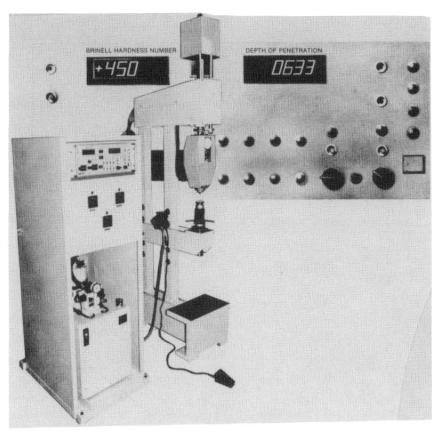

Source: MEI Course 12, "Mechanical Testing of Metals", Lesson 3, "Hardness Testing," ASM, 1983, p. 8

are available that may help to circumvent the above limitations. A typical portable instrument is shown in Fig. 6. This type weighs about 25 lb, so that it can be easily transported to the workpiece. Portable testers can handle a wider variety of workpieces than the stationary types. For instance, Fig. 6 shows how a portable tester is used to test a circular workpiece. The tester attaches to the workpiece like a C-clamp, with the anvil on one side of the workpiece and the indenter on the other. For very large parts, an encircling chain is used to hold the tester in place as the pressure is applied.

Fig. 6 Hydraulic, manually operated portable Brinell hardness tester

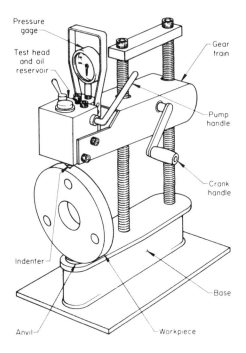

Source: MEI Course 12, "Mechanical Testing of Metals," Lesson 3, "Hardness Testing," ASM, 1983, p. 9

Portable testers generally apply the load hydraulically, using a spring-loaded relief valve. The load is applied until the relief valve opens momentarily. With this type of tester, the hydraulic pressure should be applied three times when testing steel with a 3000-kg load. This is the equivalent to a holding time of 15 s, as required by the more conventional method. For other materials and loads, comparison tests should be made to determine the number of load applications required to give results equivalent to the conventional method.

Calibration and Limits of Error. ASTM E10 specifies that a Brinell hardness tester, primarily used to make laboratory or reference tests, is acceptable for use in the loading range, in which the tester error does not exceed 1%. A tester that is used for routine testing is acceptable for use over a loading range, in which the error does not exceed 2%.

A tester should be checked by periodic calibration, preferably with a proving ring, although weights and levers may be used. The proving ring (Fig. 7) is an elastic calibration device that is placed on the anvil of the tester. The deflection of the ring under the applied load is measured by a micrometer screw and a vibrating reed, mounted diametrically in the ring. Then the amount of elastic deflection is calculated into the load in kilograms and compared to the machine's dial gage. Brinell hardness testers also may be checked by making indentations in standard test blocks of known hardness value.

Fig. 7 Proving ring used for calibrating Brinell hardness testers

Source: MEI Course 12, "Mechanical Testing of Metals," Lesson 3, "Hardness Testing," ASM, 1983, p. 10

Maintenance of Equipment. To achieve accurate results from Brinell testing, the equipment must be maintained and serviced regularly, especially for machines exposed to shop environments. The frequency of servicing depends on whether the testers are used often, as in a production line, or only occasionally. The ball indenter should be checked regularly for deformation and rotated frequently. Indenters are susceptible to wear, as well as to damage. When an indenter becomes worn or damaged, so that indentations no longer meet the standards, it must be replaced. Attempts should never be made to compensate for a worn or damaged indenter.

Precautions and Limitations

To avoid errors in Brinell hardness testing, the fundamentals and limitations of the test must be thoroughly understood. Certain guidelines must be followed:

- Indentations never should be made on a curved surface with a radius of less than 25 mm (1 in).

- Spacing of indentations must be in accordance with the above requirement.

- The load must be applied steadily to avoid overloading.

- The load should be applied so that the direction of loading is perpendicular to the workpiece surface within 2°.

- Thickness of the workpiece should be great enough so that no bulge or mark, showing the effect of the load, appears on the side of the workpiece opposite the indentation. The Brinell test is not applicable to testing thin sheet metal. Thickness of the workpiece should be approximately ten times the indentation depth. The depth of the indentation may be calculated by:

$$\text{Depth (mm)} = \frac{L}{\pi D \times (\text{HB})}$$

where L is the load in kg; D is the ball diameter in mm; and HB is the Brinell hardness number. For example, HB 300 is determined by:

$$\text{Depth} = \frac{3000}{\pi D \times 300}$$

$$\text{Depth} = \frac{1}{\pi}$$

where the minimum thickness is 3.2 mm (0.125 in.).

- The surface finish of the workpiece should be smooth enough so that the indentation is clearly outlined to permit an accurate measurement.

- The size and shape of the workpiece must be capable of accommodating relatively large indentations. Because of these relatively large indentations, the workpiece may not be usable after testing.

- The limit of the hardness range--about 16 HB minimum for the 500-kg load for soft materials to 444 HB (627 HB for a carbide indenter) maximum for the 3000-kg load for hard materials--is generally considered the practical range for the Brinell test.

Brinell Testing of Specific Materials. As is true for other indentation methods of testing hardness, the most accurate results are obtained when testing homogeneous materials, regardless of the hardness range. Hardened and tempered or annealed steels, within the above prescribed hardness ranges, are virtually all amenable to Brinell testing.

Case hardened steels, as a rule, are not suited to Brinell testing because: (1) in most instances, the hardness of case hardened parts is above the practical range for Brinell testing, and (2) the cases are rarely thick enough to provide the required support, so that "cave in" results, and in turn, grossly inaccurate readings are obtained.

Some problems are encountered when using the Brinell test for nonhomogeneous materials, such as cast irons, powder metallurgy parts, and cemented carbides. Nonferrous metals are generally amenable to Brinell testing, usually with the 500-kg load. Chapter 7 covers the methods best adapted for testing these materials.

Chapter 3

Rockwell Hardness Testing

Rockwell hardness testing is the most widely used method for determining hardness, because: (1) the Rockwell test is simple to perform and does not require highly skilled operators; (2) by using different loads and indenters, Rockwell hardness testing can be used to determine the hardness of most metals and alloys, ranging from the softest bearing materials to the hardest steels; (3) a reading can be taken in a matter of seconds with conventional manual operation and in even less time with automated setups; and (4) optical measurements are not required (all readings are direct).

Testing Principle

Rockwell hardness testing differs from Brinell testing in that the hardness is determined by the depth of indentation made by a constant load impressed upon an indenter. Although a number of different indenters are used for Rockwell hardness testing, the most common is a diamond ground to a 120° cone with a spherical apex that has a 0.2-mm (0.008-in.) radius (Fig. 1).

As shown in Fig. 1, the Rockwell hardness test consists of measuring the additional depth to which an indenter is forced by a heavy (major) load beyond the depth of a previously applied light (minor) load. Application of the minor load eliminates backlash in the load train. It also causes the indenter to break through slight surface roughness and crush particles of foreign matter, thus contributing to much greater accuracy in the test. The basic principle involving minor and major loads, shown in Fig. 1, applies to steel ball indenters, as well as to diamond indenters.

Fig. 1 Principle of the Rockwell test

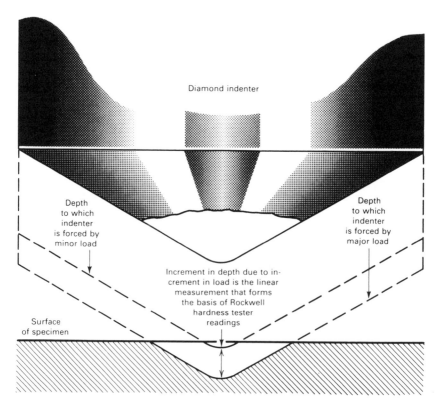

Although a diamond indenter is illustrated, the same principle applies for steel ball indenters and other loads
Source: **Metals Handbook, Mechanical Testing, Vol. 8, 9th ed.,** ASM, 1985, p. 75

The minor load is applied first, and a reference or "set" position is established on the dial gage of the Rockwell hardness tester. Then the major load is applied. Without moving the workpiece being tested, the major load is removed, and the Rockwell hardness number is automatically indicated on the dial gage. The entire operation requires only 5 to 10 s to complete.

Diamond cone indenters are used mainly for testing hard materials, such as hardened steels and cemented carbides. Hardened steel ball indenters which are available with diameters of 1.6, 3.2, 6, and 12.5 mm (1/16, 1/8, 1/4 and 1/2 in.), are used for testing softer materials, such as fully annealed steels, softer grades of cast irons, a wide variety of nonferrous metals, and some nonmetallic materials.

Basically, there are two types of Rockwell tests--Rockwell and Rockwell superficial. In Rockwell testing, the minor load is 10 kg and the major load is 60, 100, or 150 kg, regardless of the type of indenter used. In superficial Rockwell testing, the minor load is 3 kg, and major loads are 15, 30, or 45 kg.

Rockwell Testing. Rockwell values are not expressed by only a number. A letter has been assigned to each combination of major load and indenter as shown in Table 1 (left column), listing 15 combinations. Each number is suffixed by the first letter H (for hardness), then the letter R (for Rockwell), and finally the letter that indicates the scale used. For example, a value of 60 on the C scale is expressed as 60 HRC, on the B scale as 60 HRB, and so on for other combinations. Regardless of the scale used, the set position (under this condition, the minor load has been applied) is the same. When the diamond cone indenter is used, readings are taken from the black numbers on the dial gage (Table 1). However, when any of the ball indenters are used, readings are taken from the red numbers.

When the reading is taken with a diamond indenter, the Rockwell number is subtracted from 100, and the result is multiplied by the increment, which is 0.002 mm (0.00008 in.). Therefore, a reading of 60 HRC indicates an indentation depth from minor to major load of:

(100 - 60) = 40
40 x 0.002 mm (0.00008 in.) = 0.08 mm (0.0032 in.) depth

For ball indenters, the hardness number is subtracted from 130; therefore, for a dial reading of 80 HRB the depth is determined by:

(130 - 80) = 50
50 x 0.002 mm (0.00008 in.) = 0.1 mm (0.004 in.) depth

Table 1   Rockwell hardness scale designations for combinations of indenter type and major load

Scale desig- nation	Indenter Type	Diam, in.	Major load, kg	Dial figure	Scale desig- nation	Indenter Type	Diam, in.	Major load, kg
Regular Rockwell Tester					**Superficial Rockwell Tester**			
B	Ball	1/16	100	Red	15N........	N Brale	.....	15
C	Brale	....	150	Black	30N........	N Brale	.....	30
A	Brale	....	60	Black	45N........	N Brale	.....	45
D	Brale	....	100	Black	15T........	Ball	1/16	15
E	Ball	1/8	100	Red	30T........	Ball	1/16	30
F	Ball	1/16	60	Red	45T........	Ball	1/16	45
G	Ball	1/16	150	Red	15W	Ball	1/8	15
H	Ball	1/8	60	Red	30W	Ball	1/8	30
K	Ball	1/8	150	Red	45W	Ball	1/8	45
L	Ball	1/4	60	Red	15X........	Ball	1/4	15
M	Ball	1/4	100	Red	30X........	Ball	1/4	30
P	Ball	1/4	150	Red	45X........	Ball	1/4	45
R	Ball	1/2	60	Red	15Y........	Ball	1/2	15
S	Ball	1/2	100	Red	30Y........	Ball	1/2	30
V	Ball	1/2	150	Red	45Y........	Ball	1/2	45

Source: MEI Course 12, "Mechanical Testing of Metals," Lesson 3, "Hardness Testing," ASM, 1983, p. 7

Superficial Rockwell Testing. The principles involved in superficial Rockwell testing are the same as in the Rockwell tests. The indenter may be either a diamond cone or a steel ball, depending on the characteristics of the material being tested. Regardless of the load, the letter N designates the use of the diamond indenter, whereas the letters T, W, X, and Y designate steel ball indenters. Scale and load combinations for superficial testing are shown in the right column of Table 1.

Superficial Rockwell hardness values are always expressed by the number suffixed by a number and a letter that show the load and indented combination. For example, if a load of 30 kg is used with a diamond indenter, the result is reported as 80 HR30N, where H is hardness; R is Rockwell; 30 is a major load of 30 kg; and N indicates a diamond indenter.

The dial on a superficial machine has only one set of divisions; thus, all tests start with the set position of 100. In the superficial test, one number represents an indentation of 0.001 mm (0.00004 in.). Therefore, a reading of 80 HR30N indicates an indentation depth from minor to major load of:

(100 - 80) = 20
20 x 0.001 mm (0.00004 in.) = 0.02 mm (0.0008 in.)

Machines for Rockwell Testing

Fig. 2 Schematic of Rockwell testing machine

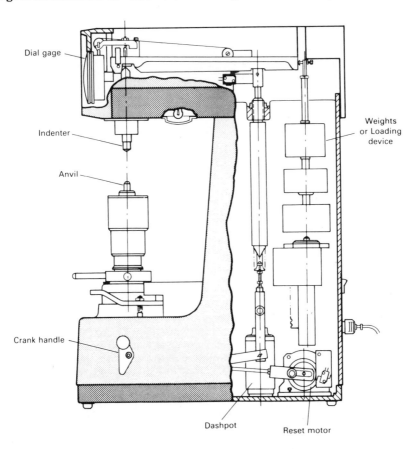

Source: **Metals Handbook, Mechanical Testing**, *Vol. 8, 9th ed.,*
ASM, 1985, p. 78

As a rule, different machines are used to make the
Rockwell and superficial Rockwell tests. However,
combination machines are available that can perform both

Fig. 3 Commonly used types of anvils designed to support various shapes of workpieces during Rockwell hardness testing

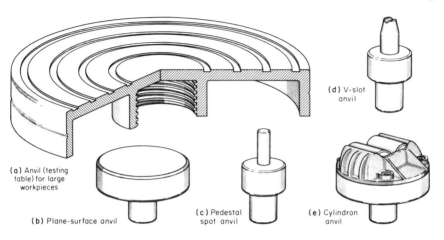

(a) Anvil (testing table) for large workpieces

(b) Plane-surface anvil

(c) Pedestal spot anvil

(d) V-slot anvil

(e) Cylindron anvil

*Source: **Metals Handbook, Mechanical Testing**, Vol. 8, 9th ed., ASM, 1985, p. 80*

Rockwell and superficial Rockwell tests. The principal components of a Rockwell tester are shown in Fig. 2. Rockwell testing machines are available with vertical capacities up to 40.6 cm (16 in.). This type of machine can accommodate a wide variety of part shapes by taking advantage of the standard, as well as special anvil designs; however, the workpiece must be held rigidly while the test is being made. A variety of anvils are illustrated in Fig. 3. The usefulness of this standard type of machine can be extended by the use of various approaches such as:

- Use of outboard or counterweighted anvil adapters for testing unwieldy workpieces, such as long shafts (Fig. 4).

- Use of a testing machine that is equipped with a clamping arrangement that applies pressure on the part from above before the indenter is brought down. This type of tester applies both minor and major loads from the top. It is especially suited for testing parts that have a large overhang or long parts, such as shafts (Fig. 5).

- Use of goose-neck anvil adapters for testing fragile cylindrical objects, as shown in Fig. 6.

Fig. 4 Setups for Rockwell hardness testing of nonstandard workpieces

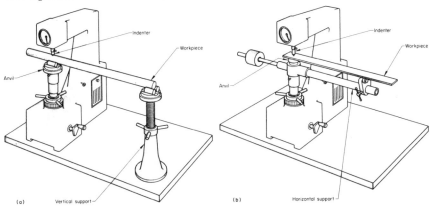

(a) Setup using an outboard vertical support for Rockwell hardness testing of long, shaftlike workpieces. (b) Horizontal support fixture for Rockwell hardness testing of relatively light long, flat, or round workpieces
Source: **Metals Handbook, Nondestructive Inspection and Quality Control**, *Vol. 11, 8th ed., ASM, 1976, p. 10*

- Use of goose-neck adapters for the indenter to test inner surfaces of cylindrical workpieces--essentially the reverse of the arrangement shown in Fig. 6.

- Use of a heavy, rigid extension bar mounted on the indenter to test inner surfaces of cylindrical workpieces (Fig. 7).

- Use of vertical supports for a large, unwieldy workpiece, as illustrated in Fig. 8. Although all hardness testers have their limitations, the workpiece shown in Fig. 8 could be tested easily in a bench-type hardness tester.

- Use of a rigid frame mounted on the indenter, which is usually constructed by the user (Fig. 9). For rapid raising or lowering of the tester, the frame can be motorized.

The number of modifications that have been or can be made to a basic Rockwell testing system is endless. Those modifications shown in Fig. 4 to 10 are intended only to illustrate some of the possibilities.

Fig. 5 Customized hardness tester

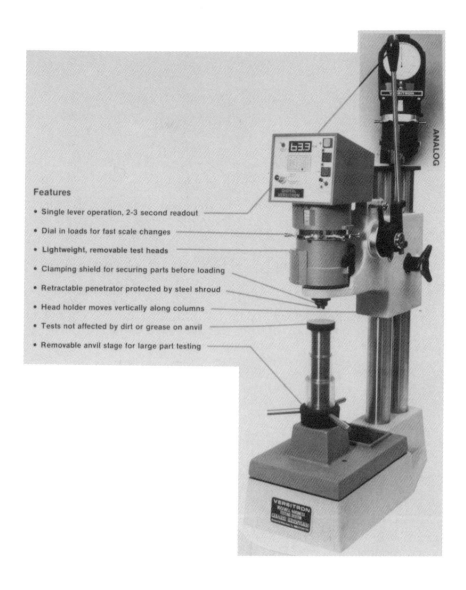

Note the retractable indenter protected by a steel shroud
Courtesy of New Age Industries, Inc.

Fig. 6 Setup for Rockwell hardness testing the outer surfaces of thin-wall cylindrical workpieces using a goose-neck adapter

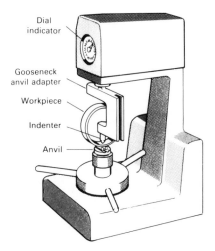

Source: **Metals Handbook, Mechanical Testing**, *Vol. 8, 9th ed., ASM, 1985, p. 11*

Fig. 7 Specially designed Rockwell hardness tester and setup for Rockwell hardness testing of inner surfaces of cylindrical workpieces

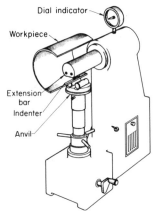

The indenter mounted in the extension bar enables tests to be made up to 146 mm (5-3/4 in.) from the end of the cylindrical workpiece
Source: **Metals Handbook, Nondestructive Inspection and Quality Control**, *Vol. 11, 8th ed., ASM, 1976, p. 11*

Fig. 8 Specially designed Rockwell hardness tester for testing large workpieces

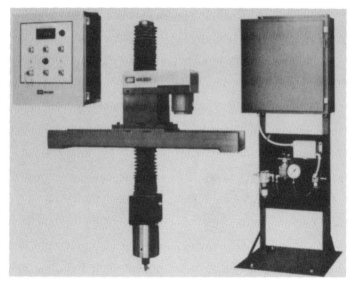

Source: *Metals Handbook, Mechanical Testing*, Vol. 8, 9th ed., ASM, 1985, p. 81

Fig. 9 Specially designed Rockwell hardness tester and setup for testing large workpieces

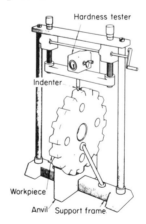

The support frame usually is designed and built by the user for specific applications
Source: *Metals Handbook, Nondestructive Inspection and Quality Control*, Vol. 11, 8th ed., ASM, 1976, p. 12

Fig. 10 Portable Rockwell hardness tester for testing large workpieces such as plates

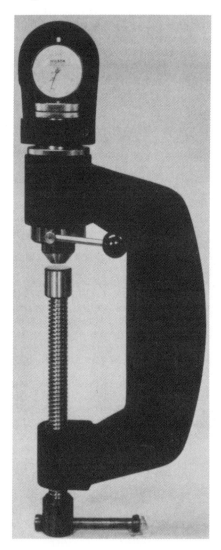

*Source: **Metals Handbook, Mechanical Testing**, Vol. 8, 9th ed., ASM, 1985, p. 79*

Mobile and Portable Hardness Testers. For hardness testing of large workpieces that cannot be moved to the hardness tester, a portable unit can be used (Fig. 10). The portable hardness tester is available in a range of sizes, up to about a 355-mm (14-in.) opening between the anvil and the indenter. All portable hardness testers are based on the Rockwell principle of minor and major loads, and the Rockwell hardness number is indicated directly on the dial gage. Operation of these testers is identical to that of bench models, except the workpiece is clamped in a C-clamp arrangement, and the indenter is recessed in a ring-type holder, which is part of the clamp. The workpiece is held by the clamp between the anvil and the holder, which, in effect, serves as an upper anvil. When the hardness test is made, the indenter is lowered to the workpiece through the holder. These hardness testers are available for either the Rockwell or superficial Rockwell scales.

Fig. 11 Typical portable hardness tester

Source: MEI Course 12, "Mechanical Testing of Metals," Lesson 3, "Hardness Testing," ASM, 1983, p. 16

Another type of portable hardness tester is shown in Fig. 11. This unit, which weighs only 7.15 kg (3.25 lb), can be used for testing various sizes and shapes of workpieces, ranging from huge gears to thin sheet. This type of instrument can be used in any position and can be operated with either diamond cone or ball indenters.

Fig. 12 Automatic Rockwell testing system for high-production work

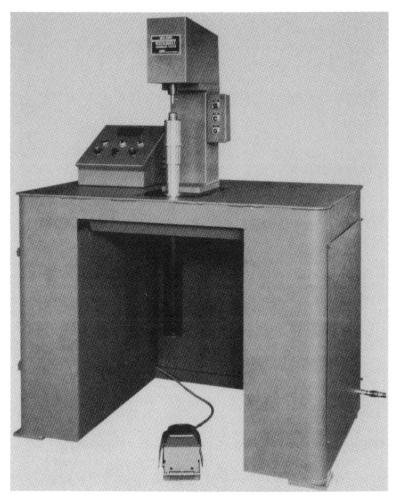

*Source: **Metals Handbook, Mechanical Testing**, Vol. 8, 9th ed., ASM, 1985, p. 79*

Production Testing. When large quantities of similar workpieces must be tested, conventional, manually operated machines may be inadequate. One approach to increase the speed of testing is to use a motorized tester. The hourly production can be increased up to 30% over the speed of a manually operated machine. Production can be accelerated using an automatic dial gage. This gage has a patented clutch-type pointer that sets automatically. When the small pointer falls anywhere within the set band, the large pointer will set automatically as the minor load is applied. Digital readout testers also are automatic.

To achieve still greater production rates a fully automated system, equipped with a digital readout, is required (Fig. 12). This setup includes a vibratory hopper into which the workpieces are dropped. From the hopper, the workpieces are individually directed onto a track and fed into the tester, one at a time. At the end of the test, the workpiece is automatically pushed into the disposal unit and classified as in tolerance, too hard, or too soft. The in-tolerance limits are set by the selector switch in the control cabinet. High and low limits can be set in increments of 0.5. For example, Rockwell numbers can have a high of 59.5 and a low of 57. Up to 1000 parts/h can be tested. An automatic feeding system can handle most workpieces.

For lower production rates, a console model may be appropriate. With this type of tester, the operation becomes automatic once the operator places the workpiece on the anvil. At the end of the test, the part is placed in the disposal unit, located within close reach, for automatic classification, while the operator positions the next part. An experienced operator can almost attain the production rate of a fully automated system.

Automatic testers are available for either Rockwell or superficial Rockwell testing, and if desired, a digital readout can be printed on chart paper. In Rockwell testing, the fastest speed is obtained with the part clamping tester that applies both minor and major load from above. A set point is not required, and the elevating screw need not be moved. The test requires only 1 s to complete (Fig. 5).

Conducting a Rockwell Test

The Rockwell test is basically simple, but accurate results depend greatly on the setup and interpretation of the results. A primary requirement is to select a type of anvil that will provide absolute rigidity for the test material during testing. A variety of anvils are available for flat workpieces, small cylindrical workpieces, large cylindrical workpieces, and other customized parts. Some typical examples are shown in Fig. 3.

The surface being tested must be perpendicular to the direction of the force on the indenter within 5° (preferably within 2°). Another consideration is that the surface of both the anvil and the workpiece surface that bears on the anvil should be free from grease and foreign material. Crushing of scale or dirt will cause an inaccurate reading. All Rockwell testers, except the top-loading type (Fig. 5), are influenced by the above factors.

The amount of surface roughness that a workpiece can tolerate depends greatly on the Rockwell scale that is being used. Generally, for a 150-kg (330-lb) load of on a diamond indenter or a 100-kg (220-lb) load on a ball indenter, a finish ground surface is sufficient to provide accurate readings. However, as lighter loads are used, the requirements for smooth surfaces become more rigorous. A 15-kg (330-lb) load usually requires a polished surface.

Careless operation in applying a load not only results in inaccurate readings, but can damage the indenter. For manually operated machines, the workpiece should be raised very slowly with the elevating screw as the workpiece approaches the indenter, and eased gently against the indenter. After the workpiece touches the indenter, the minor load is applied by forcing the workpiece against the indenter until the small hand on the dial goes slightly past the dot. At this point, the operator should be aware that several different types of Rockwell testers are available. Thus, some variation in technique is required for setting the minor load, so that the operating instructions for a specific machine should always be observed.

After the minor load is applied, the large dial is set to zero after which the major load is applied by releasing the crank (Fig. 2). When the major load is released, it *should not be touched by hand*, until the hand on the dial has come completely to rest. The operator should *never* force the crank, because inaccuracies and possible machine damage will result. After the dial has come to rest, the load should be retracted by reversing the crank. Then the reading is taken from the dial. Digital readout testers perform all of the above automatically after the minor load has been manually applied. The top-loading Rockwell tester (Fig. 5) performs the test with one operation of a loading lever, thus eliminating the multiple steps.

Selection of Rockwell Scale. Table 1 lists 30 different Rockwell scales. Correct hardness evaluations can be made only by selecting the proper scale for the test. Factors that affect the scale selection are classified as type of work metal, thickness of work metal, width of area to be tested, and scale limitations.

Table 2   Typical applications of regular Rockwell hardness scales

Scale(a)	Typical applications
B	Copper alloys, soft steels, aluminum alloys, malleable iron
C	Steel, hard cast irons, pearlitic malleable iron, titanium, deep case-hardened steel and other materials harder than HRB 100
A	Cemented carbides, thin steel and shallow case-hardened steel
D	Thin steel and medium case-hardened steel and pearlitic malleable iron
E	Cast iron, aluminum and magnesium alloys, bearing metals
F	Annealed copper alloys, thin soft sheet metals
G	Phosphor bronze, beryllium copper, malleable irons. Upper limit is HRG 92, to avoid possible flattening of ball.
H	Aluminum, zinc, lead
K, L, M, P, R, S, V	Bearing metals and other very soft or thin materials. Use smallest ball and heaviest load that do not give anvil effect.

(a) The N scales of a superficial hardness tester are used for materials similar to those tested on the Rockwell C, A, and D scales, but of thinner gage or case depth. The T scales are used for materials similar to those tested on the Rockwell B, F, and G scales, but of thinner gage. When minute indentations are required, a superficial hardness tester should be used. The W, X, and Y scales are used for very soft materials

Source: MEI Course 12, "Mechanical Testing of Metals," Lesson 3, "Hardness Testing," ASM, 1983, p. 17

Table 2 lists typical work metals and Rockwell scales commonly used for testing these materials. This information also can be used for the superficial scales. For example, the operator may note that the C, A, and D scales--all used with diamond indenters--are used for very hard materials, such as hardened steel and carbide. Therefore, any material in this category would use a diamond indenter. The operator must decide whether to use the Rockwell C, A, D, 15N, 30N, or 45N scale. When choosing a scale, it must provide the required degree of sensitivity, accuracy, and repeatability. These factors are affected by the variables that follow.

Effect of Metal Thickness. During testing, the metal surrounding a Rockwell indentation is unavoidably cold worked. The depth of the material affected by the indentation may be as much as ten times the indentation depth. Therefore, the thickness of the work metal must be at least ten times the indentation depth to obtain an accurate reading.

The depth of indentation for any Rockwell test can be computed (see the sections on indenters, loads, and scales). In practice, however, computation is not required, because applicable tables are available (Table 3). To use Table 3, assume for example that it is necessary to check the hardness of a strip of steel 0.35 mm (0.014 in.) thick with an approximate hardness of 63 HRC. From Table 3, a material having a hardness of 63 HRC must be approximately 0.71 mm (0.028 in.) thick to obtain accurate results with the C scale. Therefore, this material cannot be tested with the C scale, and other scales must be checked to determine which may be the most suitable.

The equivalent values for 63 HRC, taken from a conversion table, are 83 HRA, 70 HR45N, 80 HR30N, and 91 HR15N. For hardened 0.35-mm (0.014-in.) thick material (Table 3), there are only three scales to choose from--45N, 30N, and 15N. The 45N scale is not suitable, because the material should be at least 74 HR45N for accurate results. On the 30N scale, the material must be at least 80 HR30N, so this scale could be used. To obtain accurate results with this material thickness using the 15N scale, the material must be at least 76 HR15N, and this material is 91.5 HR15N. Therefore, either the 30N or 15N scales could be used for this specific material. When a choice exists between two scales, the one using the heavier load usually is preferred.

The above approach of determining the appropriate scale also applies to the hardness of a carburized or nitrided case;

that is, the thickness of the effective case should be considered as material thickness. It should be noted that minimum thickness tables, such as Table 3, are only guidelines to testing parameter, and each application should be evaluated individually.

Table 3   Minimum work-metal hardness values for testing various thicknesses of metals with regular and superficial Rockwell hardness testers(a)

Metal thick- ness, in.	Minimum hardness for superficial hardness testing						Minimum hardness for regular hardness testing					
	Diamond Brale indenter			Ball indenter, 1/16 in.			Diamond Brale indenter			Ball indenter, 1/16 in.		
	15N (15 kg)	30N (30 kg)	45N (45 kg)	15T (15 kg)	30T (30 kg)	45T (45 kg)	A (60 kg)	D (100 kg)	C (150 kg)	F (60 kg)	B (100 kg)	G (150 kg)
0.005	...	...	...	93	...	...	...	...	...	...	...	...
0.006	92	...	...	...	...	...	...	...	...	...	...	...
0.008	90	...	...	...	...	...	...	...	...	...	...	...
0.010	88	...	...	90	87	...	...	...	...	...	...	...
0.012	83	82	77	...	...	...	...	...	...	...	...	...
0.014	76	80	74	...	...	...	...	...	...	...	...	...
0.015	...	...	...	78	77	77	...	...	...	...	...	...
0.016	68	74	72	...	...	...	86	...	...	...	...	...
0.018	(b)	66	68	...	...	...	84	...	...	...	...	...
0.020	(b)	57	63	(b)	58	62	82	77	...	100	...	...
0.022	(b)	47	58	...	...	...	78	75	69	...	...	...
0.024	(b)	(b)	51	...	...	...	76	72	67	...	...	...
0.025	...	...	...	(b)	(b)	26	...	...	...	92	92	90
0.026	(b)	(b)	37	...	...	...	71	68	65	...	...	...
0.028	(b)	(b)	20	...	...	...	67	63	62	...	...	...
0.030	(b)	(b)	(b)	(b)	(b)	(b)	60	58	57	67	68	69
0.032	(b)	(b)	(b)	...	...	...	(b)	51	52	...	...	...
0.034	(b)	(b)	(b)	...	...	...	(b)	43	45	...	...	...
0.035	...	...	...	(b)	(b)	(b)	...	...	...	(b)	44	46
0.036	(b)	(b)	(b)	...	...	...	(b)	(b)	37	...	...	...
0.038	(b)	(b)	(b)	...	...	...	(b)	(b)	28	...	...	...
0.040	(b)	(b)	(b)	(b)	(b)	(b)	(b)	(b)	20	(b)	20	22

(a) These values are only approximate and are intended primarily as a guide; see text for example of use. Materials thinner than those shown should be tested on a microhardness tester. The thickness of the workpiece should be at least 1-1/2 times the diagonal of the indentation when using a Vickers indenter and at least 1/2 times the long diagonal when using a Knoop indenter. (b) No minimum hardness for metal of equal or greater thickness

Source: MEI Course 12, "Mechanical Testing of Metals," Lesson 3, "Hardness Testing," ASM, 1983, p. 18

After determining the scale on the basis of minimum thickness values, an actual test should be made. Then the underside directly beneath the indentation should be examined to determine if the material was disturbed or if any bulges resulted. If there is evidence of either, the material was too thin for the load applied, and a condition known as "anvil effect" has resulted. In this instance, the next lighter load should be used to conduct another test.

When anvil effect occurs, the test result will be inaccurate and the anvil may be damaged. It should be inspected immediately, and if it is marred or indented, its surface should be refinished, preferably by the manufacturer. In addition, the use of several flat workpieces, piled one on top of another, is never recommended, because slippage will occur, and a true value will be difficult to obtain.

Effect of Test Area Width and Spacing. For a workpiece of a given thickness, there are also limitations on the width of the test material. If the indentation is placed too close to the edge of a workpiece, the indentation will deform outward, and an erroneous reading will result. The distance from the center of the indentation to the edge of the workpiece must be at least 2.5 times the diameter of the indentation to ensure an accurate test. Thus, the full width of a test area must be at least 5 times the diameter of the center indentation. Although the indentation diameter can be calculated, for all practical purposes, these distances can be determined visually.

Because hardness testing cold works the surrounding material, indentations placed too close together will yield inaccurate results. The distance from center to center of indentations must be at least three indentation diameters. Specifying the spacing in terms of the indentation diameter accounts for the greater amount of cold working that occurs in soft materials, which produces larger indentations.

Limitations of Rockwell Scales. A diamond indenter should never be used when readings fall below 20 HRC (or the equivalent in other scales). Sensitivity is lessened when indenting so far down on a conical indenter. In addition to the inaccuracy which may result, there is a danger of damaging or even losing the diamond. The diamond indenter is not calibrated for values below 20 HRC. When readings drop below 20 HRC, another scale, such as A or D, should be selected. The B scale, which uses a ball-type indenter, also can be used.

There is no particular limitation on the maximum hardness that can be tested with a diamond indenter. However, the C scale should not be used for testing cemented carbides, because the carbides are likely to fracture and damage the indenter. The A scale (60-kg load) is the heaviest load that should be used for testing carbides.

Although scales for the ball indenter start at 130 (on the Rockwell machine), readings above 100 should not be accepted. Between 100 and 130, only the very tip of the ball is being used, thus resulting in poor sensitivity. Also, with the smaller diameter indenters, there is a greater likelihood of flattening the indenter with the high unit pressure developed. As readings that exceed 100 are obtained, the next heavier load or the next smaller indenter should be used. When readings that approach or go below zero are obtained, the next lighter load or the next larger indenter should be used. Reporting Rockwell readings below zero is *never* recommended.

Correction for Cylindrical Workpieces. When an indenter is forced into a convex surface, there is less lateral support supplied for the indenting force. Consequently, the indenter will sink further, if other conditions remain the same. For convex surfaces, low readings will result. On the other hand, when testing a concave surface, opposite conditions prevail; that is, abnormal lateral support is provided, and the readings will be higher than for testing the same metal with a flat surface.

For diameters of more than 25 mm (1 in.), the difference is negligible. For diameters of less than 25 mm (1 in.), especially for softer materials that involve larger indentations, the curvature, whether concave or convex, must be taken into consideration, if a comparison is to be made with different diameters or with a flat surface. Also, correction factors should be applied when workpieces are expected to meet a specified value.

Correction factors for regular and superficial Rockwell hardness values are presented in Table 4. The corrections are added to the dial gage or digital reading when testing convex surfaces and subtracted when testing concave surfaces. The regular Rockwell scales can be used for diameters down to 6.35 mm (0.25 in.); for the superficial Rockwell test, diameters down to 3.175 mm (0.125 in.) are used (Table 4). Rockwell testing of diameters smaller than 3.175 mm (0.125 in.) is not recommended. Smaller diameters may be tested by microhardness methods (see Chapter 5).

Table 4 Correction values for cylindrical workpieces tested on regular and superficial Rockwell hardness testers(a)

Regular Hardness Testing, 1/16-In. Ball Indenter (B, F and G Scales)

Observed reading	1/8	1/4	3/8	1/2	5/8	3/4	7/8	1
100		3.5	2.5	1.5	1.5	1.0	1.0	0.5
90		4.0	3.0	2.0	1.5	1.5	1.5	1.0
80		5.0	3.5	2.5	2.0	1.5	1.5	1.5
70		6.0	4.0	3.0	2.5	2.0	2.0	1.5
60		7.0	5.0	3.5	3.0	2.5	2.0	2.0
50		8.0	5.5	4.0	3.5	3.0	2.5	2.0
40		9.0	6.0	4.5	4.0	3.0	2.5	2.5
30		10.0	6.5	5.0	4.5	3.5	3.0	2.5
20		11.0	7.5	5.5	4.5	4.0	3.5	3.0
10		12.0	8.0	6.0	5.0	4.0	3.5	3.0
0		12.5	8.5	6.5	5.5	4.5	3.5	3.0

Regular Hardness Testing, Diamond Brale Indenter (C, D and A Scales)

Observed reading	1/8	1/4	3/8	1/2	5/8	3/4	7/8	1
80		0.5	0.5	0.5				
70		1.0	1.0	0.5	0.5	0.5		
60		1.5	1.0	1.0	0.5	0.5	0.5	0.5
50		2.5	2.0	1.5	1.0	0.5	0.5	0.5
40		3.5	2.5	2.0	1.5	1.0	1.0	1.0
30		5.0	3.5	2.5	2.0	1.5	1.5	1.0
20		6.0	4.5	3.5	2.5	2.0	1.5	1.5

Superficial Hardness Testing, 1/16-In. Ball Indenter (15T, 30T and 45T Scales)

Observed reading	1/8	1/4	3/8	1/2	5/8	3/4	7/8	1
90	1.5	1.0	1.0	0.5	0.5	0.5		0.5
80	3.0	2.0	1.5	1.5	1.0	1.0		0.5
70	5.0	3.5	2.5	2.0	1.5	1.0		1.0
60	6.5	4.5	3.0	2.5	2.0	1.5		1.5
50	8.5	5.5	4.0	3.0	2.5	2.0		1.5
40	10.0	6.5	4.5	3.5	3.0	2.5		2.0
30	11.5	7.5	5.0	4.0	3.5	2.5		2.0
20	13.0	9.0	6.0	4.5	3.5	3.0		2.0

Superficial Hardness Testing, Diamond Brale Indenter (15N, 30N, and 45N Scales)

Observed reading	1/8	1/4	3/8	1/2	5/8	3/4	7/8	1
90	0.5	0.5						
85	0.5	0.5	0.5					
80	1.0	0.5	0.5	0.5				
75	1.5	1.0	0.5	0.5	0.5	0.5		
70	2.0	1.0	1.0	0.5	0.5	0.5		0.5
65	2.5	1.5	1.0	0.5	0.5	0.5		0.5
60	3.0	1.5	1.0	1.0	0.5	0.5		0.5
55	3.5	2.0	1.5	1.0	1.0	0.5		0.5
50	3.5	2.0	1.5	1.0	1.0	1.0		0.5
45	4.0	2.5	2.0	1.0	1.0	1.0		1.0
40	4.5	3.0	2.0	1.5	1.0	1.0		1.0

(a) These correction values are added to the dial gage reading when hardness testing on the outer (convex) surface and subtracted when testing on the inner (concave) surface. The values are only approximate and represent the averages, to the nearest half Rockwell number, of numerous actual observations by different investigators, as well as mathematical analyses of the same problem. The accuracy of tests on cylindrical workpieces will be seriously affected by alignment of elevating screw, V-anvil and indenters, and by surface finish and straightness of the cylinders
Source: MEI Course 12, "Mechanical Testing of Metals," Lesson 3, "Hardness Testing," ASM, 1983, p. 20

Calibration and Maintenance of Rockwell Testers

If a hardness tester used constantly, checking against standard test blocks should be done every day. Use only the proper side of test block. In many shops, this checking is done at the beginning of each shift. Not only will this indicate if the tester is out of calibration, but also if the indenter has been damaged.

In some shops, checking once a day is not sufficient. For example, in one plant where several Rockwell testers are in constant use, all indenters are checked at least once per day in the tool inspection department, using a shadowgraph or similar instrument that will readily reveal any imperfections in the indenter. In addition, each indenter is checked at the beginning of each shift, using the appropriate standard test blocks; that is, test blocks that conform to the range or ranges of the test materials.

If the tester is used for a wide range of materials and hardnesses, it should be checked at the high, middle, and low ranges of the scale. For example, the C scale should be checked at approximately 63, 45, and 25 HRC. On the other hand, if only one or two ranges are used, test blocks should be chosen that fall within ±5 hardness numbers of the operating range for diamond indenters and ±10 hardness numbers for ball indenters.

Proper checking involves a minimum of five readings on the surface of the standard block. The average must fall within the tolerances stamped on the side of the test block for the tester to be considered in calibration. Only the standardized surface of the test block should be used. To avoid any error due to possible curvature of the block, use of a spot-type anvil is recommended.

If the average of five readings falls outside the limits, the difference between this average and the test block average can be noted. This error may be temporarily compensated for in evaluating results. Continued practice of compensating for an out-of-calibration tester should be discouraged. The tester should be carefully cleaned and examined according to the instruction manual. The indenter should be examined for possible damage. A defective indenter should be replaced immediately. If these approaches fail, a factory-trained representative should be consulted. General maintenance of Rockwell testers, including adjustment for speed of applying the load, should be periodic and thorough.

For test blocks, the same spacing rule applies; that is, the distance from center to center of indentations is at least three indentation diameters. An old test block that has had its indentations ground off or has indentations on both sides should never be used for calibration.

Testing of Case Hardened Steel Parts. To accurately test case hardened workpieces, the effective case depth should be at least ten times the indentation depth. Generally, cases are quite hard, so only diamond indenters are used. Therefore, one has a choice of six scales. It is highly important to select the scale that corresponds to the case depth. However, if the case depth is not known, a skilled operator can determine certain case characteristics, by using different scales and making comparisons on the conversion table. For example, a part shows a reading of 91 when measured with the 15N scale and 62 HRC. This indicates a case that is hard at the surface, as well as at an appreciable depth, because the equivalent of 62 HRC is shown as 91 HR15N. However, if the case shows 91 HR15N and only 55 HRC, it is evident that the indenter is "breaking through" a relatively thin case. Rockwell testing, by means of two or more scales, cannot replace more sophisticated methods of measuring case depth. However, the procedure described above can be used to gain immediate practical knowledge of case characteristics.

Detection of decarburization can be achieved by the indentation hardness test, essentially by reversing the technique described above for obtaining an indication of case depth. Decarburization may be detected by making two indentation tests--one by the 15N scale and another with the C scale. If the equivalent hardness is not obtained in converting from the 15N to the C scale, a decarburized layer is indicated. However, this technique is most effective for determining very thin (0.1-mm, or 0.004-in. or less) layers of decarburization.

When decarburization is present, other methods such as microhardness testing should be used to determine its extent. Such a procedure is commonly used to control neutral hardening furnaces, notably salt baths. For example, at the beginning of a shift, a wafer-thick test button of 1095 steel is quickly heated and water quenched. Then, the test pieces are tested by the C scale and should read about 65 HRC. Finally, they are tested on the 15N scale. If the reading is less than about 92 HR15N, there is evidence of decarburization, and some adjustments need to be made in the salt composition or the atmosphere before valuable parts are placed in the furnace. However, decarburization can be responsible for gross errors in indentation hardness testing.

The technique described above also may be used to detect retained austenite in surface layers, because it is a softer constituent.

Fig. 13 Apparatus for Rockwell testing at temperatures up to 760 °C (1400 °F)

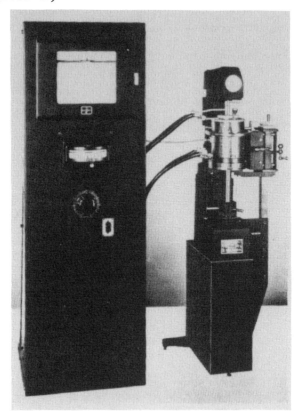

Source: **Metals Handbook, Mechanical Testing**, *Vol. 8, 9th ed., ASM, 1985, p. 83*

Rockwell Testing at Elevated Temperatures. Of the several methods that are used to determine hardness at elevated temperature, the modified Rockwell test is used most frequently. A Rockwell system for elevated temperature testing is shown in Fig. 13. Basically, this system consists of a Rockwell tester containing a built-in furnace with provisions for a controlled atmosphere (usually argon, although a vacuum furnace may be used). This furnace is connected to a temperature control system. This testing system also features an indexing fixture, which makes it possible to bring any area of the specimen under the indenter without contaminating the atmosphere or disturbing the temperature equilibrium. This arrangement permits several tests to be made on a single specimen, while maintaining the temperature and atmosphere.

One major difference in elevated temperature testing, compared with room-temperature testing, is the indenter material. Diamond indenters are not capable of withstanding the extreme temperatures involved. Consequently, sapphire or special carbide indenters are used. A typical procedure for the system illustrated in Fig. 13 is:

- Place the specimen to be tested on the table beneath the indenter. Thermocouples are inserted in this table.

- Fill the furnace chamber with argon.

- Set the temperature controller and allow the specimen to reach this temperature.

- Start the test by depressing the switch, causing the motor to lower the indenter onto the specimen. After a preset time, the indenter raises, and the value is recorded.

- Then the specimen may be indexed for additional tests, as desired.

Chapter 4

Vickers Hardness Testing

The Vickers hardness test follows the Brinell principle, in that an indenter of definite shape is pressed into the material to be tested, the load is removed, the diagonals of the resulting indentation are measured, and the hardness number is calculated by dividing the load by the surface area of indentation.

Principles of the Vickers Hardness Test. The indenter is made of diamond and is in the form of a square-based pyramid with an angle of 136° between faces (Fig. 1). This indenter thus has an angle across corners, or a so-called edge angle, of 148° 6'42.5". The facets are highly polished, free from surface imperfections, and the point is sharp. The loads applied vary from 1 to 120 kg; the standard loads are 5, 10, 20, 30, 50, 100, and 120 kg. For most hardness testing, 50 kg is maximum.

With the Vickers indenter, the depth of the indentation is about one seventh of the diagonal length of the indentation. For certain types of testing studies, there are advantages to such a shape. The Vickers hardness number (HV) is the ratio of the load applied to the indenter to the surface area of the indentation:

$$HV = 2P \sin \frac{\left(\frac{\theta}{2} \right)}{d^2} = \frac{1.8544P}{d^2}$$

where P is the applied load, in kg; d is the mean diagonal of the indentation in mm; and θ is the angle between opposite faces of the indenter (136°).

Fig. 1 Diamond pyramid indenter used for Vickers testing and resulting indentation in the workpiece

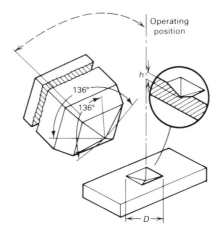

D is the mean diagonal of the indentation in millimeters
*Source: **Metals Handbook, Mechanical Testing**, Vol. 8, 9th ed., ASM, 1985, p. 91*

Equipment for Vickers Testing

Equipment for performing the Vickers test should be designed to apply the load without impact, and friction should be reduced to a minimum. The actual load on the indenter should be correct to less than 1%, and the load should be applied slowly, because the Vickers is a static test. Some standards require that the full load be maintained for 15 s.

To obtain the greatest accuracy in hardness testing, the applied load should be as large as possible, consistent with the dimensions of the workpiece. Loads of more than 50 kg are likely to fracture the diamond, particularly when used on hard materials.

The accuracy of the micrometer microscope should be checked against a stage micrometer, which consists of ruled lines, usually 0.1 mm (0.004 in.) apart, that have been checked against certified length standards. The average length of the two diagonals is used to determine the hardness value.

The corners of the indentation provide indicators of the length of the diagonals. The area must be calculated from the average of readings of both diagonals. The indentations usually are measured under vertical illumination with a magnification of about 125 diameters.

The included angle of the diamond indenter should be 136°, with a tolerance of less than $^+_-1°$, which is readily obtainable with modern diamond-grinding equipment. This would yield an error of less than 1% in the hardness number. The indenters must be controlled carefully during manufacture, so that the indentations produced will be symmetrical. Also no offset should exist at the apex of the diamond. As is true for Brinell testing, tables are available for converting the values of the measured diagonals of the indentation in microns to a Vickers (Diamond Pyramid) hardness number (see Table 1). Examples are presented in Table 1 to show how the Diamond Pyramid number is calculated from the diagonal measurement and applied load. This table is also applicable for microhardness testing when the Vickers indenter is used.

Table 1 Diamond pyramid hardness numbers for load of 1 gf

Diagonal of Indentation (Microns)	Diamond Pyramid Hardness Number for Diagonal Measured to 0.1 Micron									
	.0	.1	.2	.3	.4	.5	.6	.7	.8	.9
1.—	1854.	1533.	1288.	1097.	946.1	824.2	724.4	641.6	572.3	513.7
2.—	463.6	420.5	383.1	350.5	321.9	296.7	274.3	254.4	236.5	220.5
3.—	206.0	193.0	181.1	170.3	160.4	151.4	143.1	135.5	128.4	121.9
4.—	115.9	110.3	105.1	100.3	95.78	91.57	87.64	83.95	80.48	77.23
5.—	74.17	71.29	68.58	66.01	63.59	61.30	59.13	57.07	55.12	53.27
6.—	51.51	49.83	48.24	46.72	45.27	43.89	42.57	41.31	40.10	38.95
7.—	37.84	36.79	35.77	34.80	33.86	32.97	32.10	31.28	30.48	29.71
8.—	28.97	28.26	27.58	26.92	26.28	25.67	25.07	24.50	23.95	23.41
9.—	22.89	22.39	21.91	21.44	20.99	20.55	20.12	19.71	19.31	18.92
10.—	18.54	18.18	17.82	17.48	17.14	16.82	16.50	16.20	15.90	15.61
11.—	15.33	15.05	14.78	14.52	14.27	14.02	13.78	13.55	13.32	13.09
12.—	12.88	12.67	12.46	12.26	12.06	11.87	11.68	11.50	11.32	11.14
13.—	10.97	10.81	10.64	10.48	10.33	10.17	10.03	9.880	9.737	9.598
14.—	9.461	9.327	9.196	9.068	8.943	8.820	8.699	8.581	8.466	8.353
15.—	8.242	8.133	8.026	7.922	7.819	7.718	7.620	7.523	7.428	7.335
16.—	7.244	7.154	7.066	6.979	6.895	6.811	6.729	6.649	6.570	6.493
17.—	6.416	6.342	6.268	6.196	6.125	6.055	5.986	5.919	5.853	5.787
18.—	5.723	5.660	5.598	5.537	5.477	5.418	5.360	5.303	5.247	5.191
19.—	5.137	5.083	5.030	4.978	4.927	4.877	4.827	4.778	4.730	4.683
20.—	4.636	4.590	4.545	4.500	4.456	4.413	4.370	4.328	4.286	4.245
21.—	4.205	4.165	4.126	4.087	4.049	4.012	3.975	3.938	3.902	3.866
22.—	3.831	3.797	3.763	3.729	3.696	3.663	3.631	3.599	3.567	3.536
23.—	3.505	3.475	3.445	3.416	3.387	3.358	3.329	3.301	3.274	3.246
24.—	3.219	3.193	3.166	3.140	3.115	3.089	3.064	3.039	3.015	2.991

Table 1 (Continued) Diamond pyramid hardness numbers for load of 1 gf

Diagonal of Indentation (Microns)	Diamond Pyramid Hardness Number for Diagonal Measured to 0.1 Micron									
	.0	.1	.2	.3	.4	.5	.6	.7	.8	.9
25.—	2.967	2.943	2.920	2.897	2.874	2.852	2.830	2.808	2.786	2.764
26.—	2.743	2.722	2.701	2.681	2.661	2.641	2.621	2.601	2.582	2.563
27.—	2.544	2.525	2.506	2.488	2.470	2.452	2.434	2.417	2.399	2.382
28.—	2.365	2.348	2.332	2.315	2.299	2.283	2.267	2.251	2.236	2.220
29.—	2.205	2.190	2.175	2.160	2.145	2.131	2.116	2.102	2.088	2.074
30.—	2.060	2.047	2.033	2.020	2.077	1.993	1.980	1.968	1.955	1.942
31.—	1.930	1.917	1.905	1.893	1.881	1.869	1.857	1.845	1.834	1.822
32.—	1.811	1.800	1.788	1.777	1.766	1.756	1.745	1.734	1.724	1.713
33.—	1.703	1.693	1.682	1.672	1.662	1.652	1.643	1.633	1.623	1.614
34.—	1.604	1.595	1.585	1.576	1.567	1.558	1.549	1.540	1.531	1.522
35.—	1.514	1.505	1.497	1.488	1.480	1.471	1.463	1.455	1.447	1.439
36.—	1.431	1.423	1.415	1.407	1.400	1.392	1.384	1.377	1.369	1.362
37.—	1.355	1.347	1.340	1.333	1.326	1.319	1.312	1.305	1.298	1.291
38.—	1.284	1.277	1.271	1.264	1.258	1.251	1.245	1.238	1.232	1.225
39.—	1.219	1.213	1.207	1.201	1.195	1.189	1.183	1.177	1.171	1.165
40.—	1.159	1.153	1.147	1.142	1.136	1.131	1.125	1.119	1.114	1.109
41.—	1.103	1.098	1.092	1.087	1.082	1.077	1.072	1.066	1.061	1.056
42.—	1.051	1.046	1.041	1.036	1.031	1.027	1.022	1.017	1.012	1.008
43.—	1.003	0.9983	0.9936	0.9891	0.9845	0.9800	0.9755	0.9710	0.9666	0.9622
44.—	0.9578	0.9535	0.9492	0.9449	0.9407	0.9364	0.9322	0.9281	0.9239	0.9198
45.—	0.9157	0.9117	0.9077	0.9036	0.8997	0.8957	0.8918	0.8879	0.8840	0.8802
46.—	0.8764	0.8726	0.8688	0.8650	0.8613	0.8576	0.8539	0.8503	0.8467	0.8430
47.—	0.8395	0.8359	0.8324	0.8288	0.8254	0.8219	0.8184	0.8150	0.8116	0.8082
48.—	0.8048	0.8015	0.7982	0.7949	0.7916	0.7883	0.7851	0.7819	0.7787	0.7755
49.—	0.7723	0.7692	0.7661	0.7630	0.7599	0.7568	0.7538	0.7507	0.7477	0.7447
50.—	0.7417	0.7388	0.7359	0.7329	0.7300	0.7271	0.7243	0.7214	0.7186	0.7158
51.—	0.7129	0.7102	0.7074	0.7046	0.7019	0.6992	0.6965	0.6938	0.6911	0.6884
52.—	0.6858	0.6832	0.6805	0.6779	0.6754	0.6728	0.6702	0.6677	0.6652	0.6627
53.—	0.6602	0.6577	0.6552	0.6527	0.6503	0.6479	0.6455	0.6431	0.6407	0.6383
54.—	0.6359	0.6336	0.6312	0.6289	0.6266	0.6243	0.6220	0.6198	0.6175	0.6153
55.—	0.6130	0.6108	0.6086	0.6064	0.6042	0.6020	0.5999	0.5977	0.5956	0.5934
56.—	0.5913	0.5892	0.5871	0.5850	0.5830	0.5809	0.5788	0.5768	0.5748	0.5728
57.—	0.5708	0.5688	0.5668	0.5648	0.5628	0.5609	0.5589	0.5570	0.5551	0.5531
58.—	0.5512	0.5493	0.5475	0.5456	0.5437	0.5419	0.5400	0.5382	0.5363	0.5345
59.—	0.5327	0.5309	0.5291	0.5273	0.5256	0.5238	0.5220	0.5203	0.5186	0.5168
60.—	0.5151	0.5134	0.5117	0.5100	0.5083	0.5066	0.5050	0.5033	0.5016	0.5000
61.—	0.4984	0.4967	0.4951	0.4935	0.4919	0.4903	0.4887	0.4871	0.4855	0.4840
62.—	0.4824	0.4809	0.4793	0.4778	0.4762	0.4747	0.4732	0.4717	0.4702	0.4687
63.—	0.4672	0.4657	0.4643	0.4628	0.4613	0.4599	0.4584	0.4570	0.4556	0.4541
64.—	0.4527	0.4513	0.4499	0.4485	0.4471	0.4457	0.4444	0.4430	0.4416	0.4403
65.—	0.4389	0.4376	0.4362	0.4349	0.4336	0.4322	0.4309	0.4296	0.4283	0.4270
66.—	0.4257	0.4244	0.4231	0.4219	0.4206	0.4193	0.4181	0.4168	0.4156	0.4143
67.—	0.4131	0.4119	0.4106	0.4094	0.4082	0.4070	0.4058	0.4046	0.4034	0.4022
68.—	0.4010	0.3999	0.3987	0.3975	0.3964	0.3952	0.3941	0.3929	0.3918	0.3906
69.—	0.3895	0.3884	0.3872	0.3861	0.3850	0.3839	0.3828	0.3817	0.3806	0.3795
70.—	0.3884	0.3774	0.3763	0.3752	0.3742	0.3731	0.3720	0.3710	0.3699	0.3689
71.—	0.3679	0.3668	0.3658	0.3648	0.3638	0.3627	0.3617	0.3607	0.3597	0.3587
72.—	0.3577	0.3567	0.3557	0.3548	0.3538	0.3528	0.3518	0.3509	0.3499	0.3489
73.—	0.3480	0.3470	0.3461	0.3451	0.3442	0.3433	0.3423	0.3414	0.3405	0.3396
74.—	0.3386	0.3377	0.3368	0.3359	0.3350	0.3341	0.3332	0.3323	0.3314	0.3305
75.—	0.3297	0.3288	0.3279	0.3270	0.3262	0.3253	0.3245	0.3236	0.3227	0.3219
76.—	0.3211	0.3202	0.3194	0.3185	0.3177	0.3169	0.3160	0.3152	0.3144	0.3136
77.—	0.3128	0.3120	0.3111	0.3103	0.3095	0.3087	0.3079	0.3072	0.3064	0.3056
78.—	0.3048	0.3040	0.3032	0.3025	0.3017	0.3009	0.3002	0.2994	0.2986	0.2979
79.—	0.2971	0.2964	0.2956	0.2949	0.2941	0.2934	0.2927	0.2919	0.2912	0.2905
80.—	0.2897	0.2890	0.2883	0.2876	0.2869	0.2862	0.2855	0.2847	0.2840	0.2833
81.—	0.2826	0.2819	0.2812	0.2806	0.2799	0.2792	0.2785	0.2778	0.2771	0.2765
82.—	0.2758	0.2751	0.2744	0.2738	0.2731	0.2725	0.2718	0.2711	0.2705	0.2698
83.—	0.2692	0.2685	0.2679	0.2672	0.2666	0.2660	0.2653	0.2647	0.2641	0.2634
84.—	0.2628	0.2622	0.2616	0.2609	0.2603	0.2597	0.2591	0.2585	0.2579	0.2573
85.—	0.2567	0.2561	0.2555	0.2549	0.2543	0.2537	0.2531	0.2525	0.2519	0.2513
86.—	0.2507	0.2501	0.2496	0.2490	0.2484	0.2478	0.2473	0.2467	0.2461	0.2456
87.—	0.2450	0.2444	0.2439	0.2433	0.2428	0.2422	0.2417	0.2411	0.2406	0.2400
88.—	0.2395	0.2389	0.2384	0.2378	0.2373	0.2368	0.2362	0.2357	0.2352	0.2346
89.—	0.2341	0.2336	0.2331	0.2325	0.2320	0.2315	0.2310	0.2305	0.2300	0.2294
90.—	0.2289	0.2284	0.2279	0.2274	0.2269	0.2264	0.2259	0.2254	0.2249	0.2244
91.—	0.2239	0.2234	0.2230	0.2225	0.2220	0.2215	0.2210	0.2205	0.2200	0.2196

Table 1 (Continued) Diamond pyramid hardness numbers for load of 1 gf

Diagonal of Indentation (Microns)	Diamond Pyramid Hardness Number for Diagonal Measured to 0.1 Micron									
	.0	.1	.2	.3	.4	.5	.6	.7	.8	.9
92.—	0.2191	0.2186	0.2181	0.2177	0.2172	0.2167	0.2163	0.2158	0.2153	0.2149
93.—	0.2144	0.2139	0.2135	0.2130	0.2126	0.2121	0.2117	0.2112	0.2108	0.2103
94.—	0.2099	0.2094	0.2090	0.2085	0.2081	0.2077	0.2072	0.2068	0.2063	0.2059
95.—	0.2055	0.2050	0.2046	0.2042	0.2038	0.2033	0.2029	0.2025	0.2021	0.2016
96.—	0.2012	0.2008	0.2004	0.2000	0.1995	0.1991	0.1987	0.1983	0.1979	0.1975
97.—	0.1971	0.1967	0.1963	0.1959	0.1955	0.1951	0.1947	0.1943	0.1939	0.1935
98.—	0.1931	0.1927	0.1923	0.1919	0.1915	0.1911	0.1907	0.1904	0.1900	0.1896
99.—	0.1892	0.1888	0.1884	0.1881	0.1877	0.1873	0.1869	0.1866	0.1862	0.1858
100.—	0.1854⁻	0.1851	0.1847	0.1843	0.1840	0.1836	0.1832	0.1829	0.1825	0.1821
101.—	0.1818	0.1814	0.1811	0.1807	0.1804	0.1800	0.1796	0.1793	0.1789	0.1786
102.—	0.1782	0.1779	0.1775	0.1772	0.1769	0.1765	0.1762	0.1758	0.1755	0.1751
103.—	0.1748	0.1745	0.1741	0.1738	0.1734	0.1731	0.1728	0.1724	0.1721	0.1718
104.—	0.1715	0.1711	0.1708	0.1705	0.1701	0.1698	0.1695	0.1692	0.1688	0.1685
105.—	0.1682	0.1679	0.1676	0.1672	0.1669	0.1666	0.1663	0.1660	0.1657	0.1654
106.—	0.1650	0.1647	0.1644	0.1641	0.1638	0.1635	0.1632	0.1629	0.1626	0.1623
107.—	0.1620	0.1617	0.1614	0.1611	0.1608	0.1605	0.1602	0.1599	0.1596	0.1593
108.—	0.1590	0.1587	0.1584	0.1581	0.1578	0.1575	0.1572	0.1569	0.1567	0.1564
109.—	0.1561	0.1558	0.1555	0.1552	0.1549	0.1547	0.1544	0.1541	0.1538	0.1535
110.—	0.1533	0.1530	0.1527	0.1524	0.1521	0.1519	0.1516	0.1513	0.1511	0.1508
111.—	0.1505	0.1502	0.1500	0.1497	0.1494	0.1492	0.1489	0.1486	0.1484	0.1481
112.—	0.1478	0.1476	0.1473	0.1470	0.1468	0.1465	0.1463	0.1460	0.1457	0.1455
113.—	0.1452	0.1450	0.1447	0.1445	0.1442	0.1440	0.1437	0.1434	0.1432	0.1429
114.—	0.1427	0.1424	0.1422	0.1419	0.1417	0.1414	0.1412	0.1410	0.1407	0.1405
115.—	0.1402	0.1400	0.1397	0.1395	0.1393	0.1390	0.1388	0.1385	0.1383	0.1381
116.—	0.1378	0.1376	0.1373	0.1371	0.1369	0.1366	0.1364	0.1362	0.1359	0.1357
117.—	0.1355	0.1352	0.1350	0.1348	0.1345	0.1343	0.1341	0.1339	0.1336	0.1334
118.—	0.1332	0.1330	0.1327	0.1325	0.1323	0.1321	0.1318	0.1316	0.1314	0.1312
119.—	0.1310	0.1307	0.1305	0.1303	0.1301	0.1299	0.1296	0.1294	0.1292	0.1290
120.—	0.1288	0.1286	0.1284	0.1281	0.1279	0.1277	0.1275	0.1273	0.1271	0.1269
121.—	0.1267	0.1265	0.1262	0.1260	0.1258	0.1256	0.1254	0.1252	0.1250	0.1248
122.—	0.1246	0.1244	0.1242	0.1240	0.1238	0.1236	0.1234	0.1232	0.1230	0.1228
123.—	0.1226	0.1224	0.1222	0.1220	0.1218	0.1216	0.1214	0.1212	0.1210	0.1208
124.—	0.1206	0.1204	0.1202	0.1200	0.1198	0.1196	0.1194	0.1193	0.1191	0.1189
125.—	0.1187	0.1185	0.1183	0.1181	0.1179	0.1177	0.1176	0.1174	0.1172	0.1170
126.—	0.1168	0.1166	0.1164	0.1163	0.1161	0.1159	0.1157	0.1155	0.1153	0.1152
127.—	0.1150	0.1148	0.1146	0.1144	0.1143	0.1141	0.1139	0.1137	0.1135	0.1134
128.—	0.1132	0.1130	0.1128	0.1127	0.1125	0.1123	0.1121	0.1120	0.1118	0.1116
129.—	0.1114	0.1113	0.1111	0.1109	0.1108	0.1106	0.1104	0.1102	0.1101	0.1099
130.—	0.1097	0.1096	0.1094	0.1092	0.1091	0.1089	0.1087	0.1086	0.1084	0.1082
131.—	0.1081	0.1079	0.1077	0.1076	0.1074	0.1072	0.1071	0.1069	0.1068	0.1066
132.—	0.1064	0.1063	0.1061	0.1059	0.1058	0.1056	0.1055	0.1053	0.1052	0.1050
133.—	0.1048	0.1047	0.1045	0.1044	0.1042	0.1041	0.1039	0.1037	0.1036	0.1034
134.—	0.1033	0.1031	0.1030	0.1028	0.1027	0.1025	0.1024	0.1022	0.1021	0.1019
135.—	0.1018	0.1016	0.1015	0.1013	0.1012	0.1010	0.1009	0.1007	0.1006	0.1004
136.—	0.1003	0.1001	0.1000	0.0998	0.0997	0.0995	0.0994	0.0992	0.0991	0.0989
137.—	0.0988	0.0987	0.0985	0.0984	0.0982	0.0981	0.0979	0.0978	0.0977	0.0975
138.—	0.0974	0.0972	0.0971	0.0970	0.0968	0.0967	0.0965	0.0964	0.0963	0.0961
139.—	0.0960	0.0958	0.0957	0.0956	0.0954	0.0953	0.0952	0.0950	0.0949	0.0948
140.—	0.0946	0.0945	0.0943	0.0942	0.0941	0.0939	0.0938	0.0937	0.0935	0.0934
141.—	0.0933	0.0931	0.0930	0.0929	0.0928	0.0926	0.0925	0.0924	0.0922	0.0921
142.—	0.0920	0.0918	0.0917	0.0916	0.0915	0.0913	0.0912	0.0911	0.0909	0.0908
143.—	0.0907	0.0906	0.0904	0.0903	0.0902	0.0901	0.0899	0.0898	0.0897	0.0896
144.—	0.0894	0.0893	0.0892	0.0891	0.0889	0.0888	0.0887	0.0886	0.0884	0.0883
145.—	0.0882	0.0881	0.0880	0.0878	0.0877	0.0876	0.0875	0.0874	0.0872	0.0871
146.—	0.0870	0.0869	0.0868	0.0866	0.0865	0.0864	0.0863	0.0862	0.0861	0.0859
147.—	0.0858	0.0857	0.0856	0.0855	0.0854	0.0852	0.0851	0.0850	0.0849	0.0848
148.—	0.0847	0.0845	0.0844	0.0843	0.0842	0.0841	0.0840	0.0839	0.0838	0.0836
149.—	0.0835	0.0834	0.0833	0.0832	0.0831	0.0830	0.0829	0.0828	0.0826	0.0825
150.—	0.0824	0.0823	0.0822	0.0821	0.0820	0.0819	0.0818	0.0817	0.0815	0.0814
151.—	0.0813	0.0812	0.0811	0.0810	0.0809	0.0808	0.0807	0.0806	0.0805	0.0804
152.—	0.0803	0.0802	0.0801	0.0800	0.0798	0.0797	0.0796	0.0795	0.0794	0.0793
153.—	0.0792	0.0791	0.0790	0.0789	0.0788	0.0787	0.0786	0.0785	0.0784	0.0783
154.—	0.0782	0.0781	0.0780	0.0779	0.0778	0.0777	0.0776	0.0775	0.0774	0.0773
155.—	0.0772	0.0771	0.0770	0.0769	0.0768	0.0767	0.0766	0.0765	0.0764	0.0763
156.—	0.0762	0.0761	0.0760	0.0759	0.0758	0.0757	0.0756	0.0755	0.0754	0.0753
157.—	0.0752	0.0751	0.0750	0.0749	0.0749	0.0748	0.0747	0.0746	0.0745	0.0744
158.—	0.0743	0.0742	0.0741	0.0740	0.0739	0.0738	0.0737	0.0736	0.0735	0.0734

Table 1 (Continued) Diamond pyramid hardness numbers for load of 1 gf

Diagonal of Indentation (Microns)	Diamond Pyramid Hardness Number for Diagonal Measured to 0.1 Micron									
	.0	.1	.2	.3	.4	.5	.6	.7	.8	.9
159.—	0.0734	0.0733	0.0732	0.0731	0.0730	0.0729	0.0728	0.0727	0.0726	0.0725
160.—	0.0724	0.0724	0.0723	0.0722	0.0721	0.0720	0.0719	0.0718	0.0717	0.0716
161.—	0.0715	0.0715	0.0714	0.0713	0.0712	0.0711	0.0710	0.0709	0.0708	0.0708
162.—	0.0707	0.0706	0.0705	0.0704	0.0703	0.0702	0.0701	0.0701	0.0700	0.0699
163.—	0.0698	0.0697	0.0696	0.0695	0.0695	0.0694	0.0693	0.0692	0.0691	0.0690
164.—	0.0690	0.0689	0.0688	0.0687	0.0686	0.0685	0.0684	0.0684	0.0683	0.0682
165.—	0.0681	0.0680	0.0680	0.0679	0.0678	0.0677	0.0676	0.0675	0.0675	0.0674
166.—	0.0673	0.0672	0.0671	0.0671	0.0670	0.0669	0.0668	0.0667	0.0667	0.0666
167.—	0.0665	0.0664	0.0663	0.0663	0.0662	0.0661	0.0660	0.0659	0.0659	0.0658
168.—	0.0657	0.0656	0.0656	0.0655	0.0654	0.0653	0.0652	0.0652	0.0651	0.0650
169.—	0.0649	0.0649	0.0648	0.0647	0.0646	0.0645	0.0645	0.0644	0.0643	0.0642
170.—	0.0642	0.0641	0.0640	0.0639	0.0639	0.0638	0.0637	0.0636	0.0636	0.0635
171.—	0.0634	0.0633	0.0633	0.0632	0.0631	0.0631	0.0630	0.0629	0.0628	0.0628
172.—	0.0627	0.0626	0.0625	0.0625	0.0624	0.0623	0.0623	0.0622	0.0621	0.0620
173.—	0.0620	0.0619	0.0618	0.0617	0.0617	0.0616	0.0615	0.0615	0.0614	0.0613
174.—	0.0613	0.0612	0.0611	0.0610	0.0610	0.0609	0.0608	0.0608	0.0607	0.0606
175.—	0.0606	0.0605	0.0604	0.0603	0.0603	0.0602	0.0601	0.0601	0.0600	0.0599
176.—	0.0599	0.0598	0.0597	0.0597	0.0596	0.0595	0.0595	0.0594	0.0593	0.0593
177.—	0.0592	0.0591	0.0591	0.0590	0.0589	0.0589	0.0588	0.0587	0.0587	0.0586
178.—	0.0585	0.0585	0.0584	0.0583	0.0583	0.0582	0.0581	0.0581	0.0580	0.0579
179.—	0.0579	0.0578	0.0578	0.0577	0.0576	0.0576	0.0575	0.0574	0.0574	0.0573
180.—	0.0572	0.0572	0.0571	0.0570	0.0570	0.0569	0.0569	0.0568	0.0567	0.0567
181.—	0.0566	0.0565	0.0565	0.0564	0.0564	0.0563	0.0562	0.0562	0.0561	0.0560
182.—	0.0560	0.0559	0.0559	0.0558	0.0557	0.0557	0.0556	0.0556	0.0555	0.0554
183.—	0.0554	0.0553	0.0553	0.0552	0.0551	0.0551	0.0550	0.0550	0.0549	0.0548
184.—	0.0548	0.0547	0.0547	0.0546	0.0545	0.0545	0.0544	0.0544	0.0543	0.0542
185.—	0.0542	0.0541	0.0541	0.0540	0.0540	0.0539	0.0538	0.0538	0.0537	0.0537
186.—	0.0536	0.0535	0.0535	0.0534	0.0534	0.0533	0.0533	0.0532	0.0531	0.0531
187.—	0.0530	0.0530	0.0529	0.0529	0.0528	0.0528	0.0527	0.0526	0.0526	0.0525
188.—	0.0525	0.0524	0.0524	0.0523	0.0522	0.0522	0.0521	0.0521	0.0520	0.0520
189.—	0.0519	0.0519	0.0518	0.0518	0.0517	0.0516	0.0516	0.0515	0.0515	0.0514
190.—	0.0514	0.0513	0.0513	0.0512	0.0512	0.0511	0.0510	0.0510	0.0509	0.0509
191.—	0.0508	0.0508	0.0507	0.0507	0.0506	0.0506	0.0505	0.0505	0.0504	0.0504
192.—	0.0503	0.0503	0.0502	0.0502	0.0501	0.0500	0.0500	0.0499	0.0499	0.0498
193.—	0.0498	0.0497	0.0497	0.0496	0.0496	0.0495	0.0495	0.0494	0.0494	0.0493
194.—	0.0493	0.0492	0.0492	0.0491	0.0491	0.0490	0.0490	0.0489	0.0489	0.0488
195.—	0.0488	0.0487	0.0487	0.0486	0.0486	0.0485	0.0485	0.0484	0.0484	0.0483
196.—	0.0483	0.0482	0.0482	0.0481	0.0481	0.0480	0.0480	0.0479	0.0479	0.0478
197.—	0.0478	0.0477	0.0477	0.0476	0.0476	0.0475	0.0475	0.0474	0.0474	0.0474
198.—	0.0473	0.0473	0.0472	0.0472	0.0471	0.0471	0.0470	0.0470	0.0469	0.0469
199.—	0.0468	0.0468	0.0467	0.0467	0.0466	0.0466	0.0465	0.0465	0.0465	0.0464
200.—	0.0464	0.0463	0.0463	0.0462	0.0462	0.0461	0.0461	0.0460	0.0460	0.0459

Source: MEI Course 12, "Mechanical Testing of Metals," Lesson 3, "Hardness Testing," ASM, 1983, pp. 33-36

Several types of hardness testers have proved acceptable for making the Vickers test in accordance with the above requirements. One type is illustrated in Fig. 2. This hardness tester, which has a main frame section that carries the stage and a starting handle with a 20-to-1 ratio, applies the load through a thrust rod to a tube, which is free to reciprocate vertically and which carries the Vickers indenter at its lower end. Attached to the main frame is a smaller frame that contains the control mechanism. The plunger reciprocates vertically under the influence of a rotating cam, to apply and release the test load. The cam is mounted on a drum, and when the starting handle has been depressed, the cam is rotated by a weight attached by a flexible wire. The speed of rotation is controlled by a piston and an oil-filled dashpot. The rate of displacement of the oil is regulated by an adjustable control valve. The plunger carries a rubber pad at its upper end, which engages with a cone mounted in the beam, thereby ensuring a very slow and diminishing rate of application for the last portion of the loading cycle. Because the cam both lowers and raises the plunger, errors due to inertia and premature load removal are eliminated.

Fig. 2 Principal component of one type of Vickers hardness tester

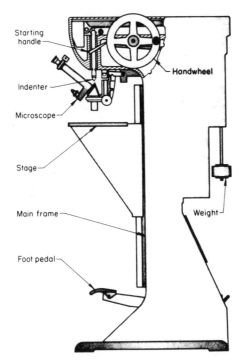

Source: MEI Course 12, "Mechanical Testing of Metals," Lesson 3, "Hardness Testing," ASM, 1983, p. 23

The microscope usually is mounted on a hinged bracket and may be moved to position over the indentation after the workpiece has been lowered sufficiently to clear the microscope. A knife-edge type of micrometer ocular is provided, and the indentations are read to knife-edges. The readings are taken from a digital counter mounted on the microscope. Tables for converting digital readings to Vickers hardness numbers are supplied (see Table 1). The micrometer ocular may be rotated through 90°, so that each diagonal may be measured.

Making the Vickers Test. In use, the workpiece is placed on the stage, which is raised by a handwheel on the side of the hardness tester until the workpiece nearly touches the diamond indenter. The load is applied by tripping the starting handle. The time taken in the application and duration of the load may be adjusted by the oil control valve in the dashpot within a range of 10 to 30 s minimum.

If the workpiece has not been elevated sufficiently for the testing load to be applied satisfactorily, a warning is given by an automatically actuated buzzer. A foot pedal readies the hardness tester for the next test after a test cycle is completed. The stage may be fitted with a V-block for supporting cylindrical work.

If routine hardness testing is to be carried out, a sliding table may be attached to the stage, and the microscope may be mounted on an auxiliary bracket on the right side of the tester, so that hardness testing may be continuous without the need for winding the stage up or down.

If desired, small-diameter balls may be used as indenters with this hardness tester. However, because it is more accurate to measure the diagonal of indentation than the diameter of a ball indentation, most workpieces, regardless of their hardness, are hardness tested with the diamond indenter.

Use of the Rockwell Superficial Hardness Tester for Vickers Tests. The Rockwell superficial hardness tester frequently is used for making tests with a Vickers indenter. Because of the design of the Rockwell tester, the loads applied are exceptionally frictionless and are applied with great accuracy. Special sets of weights for applying loads of 5 to 60 kg in steps of 5 kg are available. Likewise, a Vickers indenter mounted specifically for use with the Rockwell superficial hardness tester is available.

By using these accessories, properly adjusting the oil dashpot, applying the minor load without bringing the dial to set position, and applying and removing the major load, the hardness test is made. No dial readings are taken; the work is placed under a microscope separate from the hardness tester, the indentation is located, the diagonals are measured, and the hardness number is obtained from conversion tables. By using transferable stages or properly calibrated jigs, the indentation may be readily located. A metallurgical microscope with a filar eyepiece is used for measuring the indentation. A magnification of about 125 diameters is used, and the microscope is calibrated with a stage micrometer to transform filar division to millimeters. Conversion tables are then used to obtain the hardness number.

Chapter 5

Microhardness Testing

The term "microhardness" usually refers to indentation hardness tests made with loads that do not exceed 1 kg (1000 g). Such tests have been made with a load as light as 1 g, although the majority of microhardness tests are made with loads of 100 to 500 g. In general, the term is related to the size of the indentation rather than to the load applied.

Knoop and Vickers Microhardness Testing

In Knoop and Vickers microhardness testing, the hardness value is determined by measuring the size of the resulting unrecovered indentation with a microscope and using established formulas or conversion tables in accordance with ASTM E384.

Development of the Knoop test by the National Bureau of Standards in 1939 and the Vickers test (also called the diamond pyramid hardness test) in England in 1925 has made microhardness testing a routine procedure. Both of these tests use precisely shaped diamond indenters and various loads to determine hardness of a wide variety of materials. Microhardness testing is capable of providing information on the hardness characteristics of materials that cannot be obtained with hardness tests such as the Brinell, Rockwell, or Scleroscope.

Because of the required degree of precision for both equipment and operation, microhardness testing is usually, although not necessarily, performed in a laboratory. Such a laboratory, however, is often a process-control laboratory and may be located close to production operations. Microhardness testing is recognized as a valuable method for controlling numerous production operations in addition to its use in research applications. Specific fields of application of microhardness testing include:

- Measuring the hardness of precision workpieces that are too small to be measured by the more common hardness testing methods

- Measuring the hardness of product forms like foil or wire that are too thin or too small in diameter to be measured by the more conventional methods

- Monitoring carburizing or nitriding operations, which is usually accomplished by hardness surveys taken on cross sections of test pieces that accompany workpieces through production operations

- Measuring the hardness of individual microconstituents

- Measuring hardness close to the edges of workpieces, thus detecting undesirable surface conditions such as grinding burn and decarburization

- Measuring the hardness of surface layers such as plating or bonded layers

Indenters. Microhardness testing is done with either one of two diamond pyramid indenters--the Vickers (also referred to as Diamond Pyramid) or the Knoop. The Vickers indenter used for microhardness testing is the same geometric form as is used for conventional Vickers testing. The depth of the Vickers indentation is approximately one seventh of the diagonal.

A standard Knoop indenter is shown in Fig. 1. This rhombic-base pyramidal indenter produces a rhombic-shaped indentation that has a ratio between long and short diagonals of approximately 7 to 1. The depth of indentation is about one thirtieth of the length of the long diagonal.

Fig. 1 Pyramidal Knoop indenter and resulting indentation in the workpiece

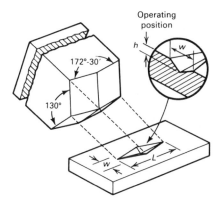

Source: **Metals Handbook, Mechanical Testing,** *Vol. 8, 9th ed., ASM, 1985, p. 91*

The Knoop hardness number (KHN or HK) is the ratio of the load applied to the indenter, P (kg) to the unrecovered projected area, A (mm^2):

$$HK = P/A = P/Cl^2$$

where P is the applied load (kg); A is the unrecovered projected area of indentation (mm^2); l is the measured length of the long diagonal (mm); and C is the indenter constant relating projected area of the indentation to the square of the length of the long diagonal (0.07028).

The choice between the Knoop and Vickers indenters is sometimes arbitrary, although because the Vickers indenter penetrates deeper into the specimen than the Knoop indenter, the Vickers is less sensitive to surface conditions. However, because the Vickers indenter has shorter diagonals, it is more sensitive to measurement errors compared to the Knoop indenter. The Knoop indenter is more widely used in the United States, whereas the Vickers indenter is more widely used in Europe.

A comparison of the shape of the indentation made by the Knoop indenter with that made by the Vickers indenter is presented in Fig. 2. Comparisons of Knoop and Vickers indentations in the same work metal with four different applied loads is shown in Fig. 3.

Fig. 2 Comparison of indentations made by Knoop and Vickers indenters

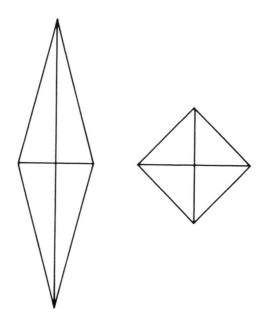

Knoop Indentation   Vickers Indentation

Source: MEI Course 12, "Mechanical Testing of Metals," Lesson 3, "Hardness Testing," ASM, 1983, p. 26

Fig. 3 Comparison of indentations made by Knoop and Vickers indenters in the same work metal and at the same loads

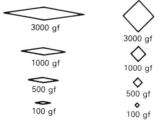

*Source: **Metals Handbook, Mechanical Testing**, Vol. 8, 9th ed., ASM, 1985, p. 90*

Microhardness Testers

Several types of microhardness testers currently are available. Most operate via the direct application of load by dead weight, or by weights and a lever. The various testers vary mainly in load range. Any can accommodate either the Knoop or the Vickers indenters. Some models are console and others are bench-mounted types.

The microhardness tester shown in Fig. 4 has a load range of 25 to 1000 g. Loads are applied by dead weight. The microscope is furnished with two objective lenses having magnification of about 175 and 500 diameters. Sources of tester error include inaccuracy in loading, vibration, rate of load application, duration of contact period, and impact. To limit the shock that can occur when the operator removes the load (this generally has an adverse effect on indentations made with loads below 500 g), an automatic test cycle is built into the microhardness tester. With this automatic test cycle, the load is applied at a constant rate, maintained in the work for 18 s, and smoothly removed. Thus, the operator does not need to touch the tester while the load is being applied and removed. The design of microhardness testers will vary from one type to another, but it is essential to remove the applied load without touching the tester if clear cut indentations are to be obtained.

A movable stage to support the workpiece is an essential component of a microhardness tester. In many applications, the indentation must be in a select area, usually limited to a few thousandths of a square millimeter. In testing with the type of microhardness tester shown in Fig. 4, first the required area is located with the microscope, then the head is shifted to make the indentation. After the indentation is made, the head is returned to its original position, so that the dimensions of the indentation can be measured with the filar eyepiece. The head of this tester can be moved with such precision that the indentation, often invisible to the naked eye, is positioned in the exact center of the field of view.

The stage can be adjusted using two micrometer screws at right angles to each other (see Fig. 4), so that a row or even a network pattern of indentations can be made with very accurate spacing, which is important in applications such as hardness surveys.

Fig. 4 Principal components of a microhardness tester

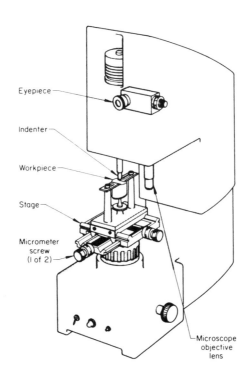

Eyepiece

Indenter

Workpiece

Stage

Micrometer
screw
(1 of 2)

Microscope
objective
lens

Source: MEI Course 12, "Mechanical Testing of Metals," Lesson 3, "Hardness Testing," ASM, 1983, p. 27

Automated setups for microhardness testing are also available. Indentations are made automatically at pre-established locations on the workpiece. Measurements can be taken as rapidly as one every 6 s (ten in less than 2 min). Various forms of readouts, including digital and printed are available. Automatic microhardness testers are relatively expensive, but their cost can often be justified when large numbers of hardness surveys are required, as in controlling case hardening operations.

Optical equipment used in microhardness testers for measuring the indentation must focus on both ends of the indentation at the same time, as well as be rigid and free from vibration. Lighting is also important. Complete specifications of measurement, including the mode of illumination, are necessary in microhardness testing. Polarized light, for instance, results in larger measurements than unpolarized light. Apparently, this is caused by the reversal of the diffraction pattern; that is, the indentation appears brighter than the background. When test data are recorded, both the magnification and the type of illumination used should be reported.

Dry objectives having the highest resolving power available generally are used, but oil immersion objectives may sometimes be necessary. For dry lenses with the highest numerical aperture that can be used, an accuracy of ± 0.5 micron has been established. Also, the same observer can compare differences between two workpieces to ± 0.2 micron accuracy. An accuracy of ± 0.3 micron on the measurement of the indentation can be achieved with an oil immersion lens, although an observer can still compare differences between two workpieces to ± 0.2 micron accuracy.

It is necessary to calibrate the optical system with great precision. A stage micrometer with a high degree of accuracy is required. Calibration must include the complete optical system used, with the filar micrometer eyepiece locked in place as it would be during the actual measurement. Also, the stage micrometer should be accurate to at least ± 0.1 micron.

Preparing and Holding the Specimen. Regardless of whether the metal being tested for microhardness is an actual workpiece or a representative specimen, surface finish is of prime importance. To permit accurate measurement of the length of the Knoop indentation or diagonals of the Vickers indentations, the indentation must be clearly defined. In general, as the test load decreases, the surface finish requirements become more stringent. When the load is 100 g or less, a metallographic finish is recommended.

In many instances, the specimen to be tested will also be used for metallographic examination, in which instance, mounting and polishing are justified. More often than not, however, mounting is not necessary, and only polishing is required.

Many types of fixtures are available for holding workpieces. Six different types are illustrated in Fig. 5. Two types of fixtures that have proved especially valuable as workpiece holders for microhardness testing are shown in Fig. 5(a) and (b). The universal clamp and leveling vise shown in

Fig. 5(a) ensures a test surface perpendicular to the indenter when mounted workpieces are used. The combination holding and polishing vise shown in Fig. 5(b) can eliminate considerable preparation time of various types of workpieces; polishing and testing can be accomplished without removing the test piece from the vise.

Fig. 5 Typical fixtures used for holding and clamping workpieces for microhardness testing

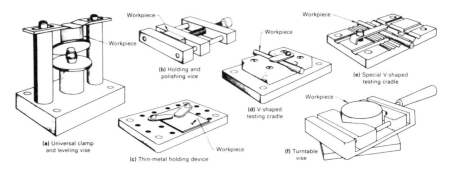

*Source: **Metals Handbook, Mechanical Testing**, Vol. 8, 9th ed., ASM, 1985, p. 96*

Other fixtures that can accommodate various types and sizes of workpieces are shown in Fig. 5(c), (d), and (e). The turntable vise shown in Fig. 5(f) is a convenient fixture for holding mounted workpieces.

Measuring the Indentation. Proper illumination is a primary requisite in measuring the indentation to maintain optimum resolution. It is also important to select a proper objective. In measuring the indentation, the ends of the indentation diagonals, regardless of whether the indentation was made by the Knoop or the Vickers indenter, must be brought into sharp focus. With the Knoop indenter, one leg of the long diagonal should never be more than 20% longer than the other. If one diagonal is abnormally long or not in focus, the surface of the workpiece should be checked to make sure it is perpendicular to the axis of the indenter. With the Vickers indenter, both diagonals should be measured and the average used for calculating the HV (DPH) value.

Determination of Hardness Number. The indentation, regardless of whether it is made by Knoop or Vickers, is measured in filar units of the measuring eyepiece. Some eyepiece-objective combinations read directly in microns, whereas others require multiplication of filar units by an objective calibration factor to convert the reading to microns. Calculations for converting the readings to Vickers numbers are given in Chapter 4. However, these calculations have been made for both Knoop and Vickers for various loads. Also available is a calculator that includes the objective calibration factor. Hardness numbers are shown in these tables for indentation readings of 1 to 200 microns for both Knoop and Vickers. Conversion to hardness number is simple. In Table 1, the Knoop hardness numbers for indentations of 1 to 200 microns are given for a load of 1 g. To determine hardness number, it is merely a matter of multiplying the micron reading by the load in grams. For example, for a diagonal reading of 100 microns using a load of 500 g, take the 1-g reading (1.423); to obtain the Knoop hardness number:

$$500 \times 1.423 = 711 \text{ HK}$$

Referring now to Table 1 in the chapter on Vickers hardness testing, assume an average diagonal reading of 40 microns. For a 1-g load, the DPH number is 1.159. Now assuming that the load is 500 g, the DPH or Vickers number is:

$$500 \times 1.159 = 579 \text{ HV}$$

Table 1   Knoop hardness numbers for load of 1 gf

Diagonal of Indentation (Microns)	Knoop Hardness Number for Diagonal Measured to 0.1 Micron									
	.0	.1	.2	.3	.4	.5	.6	.7	.8	.9
1.—	14230.	11760.	9881.	8420.	7260.	6324.	5558.	4924.	4392.	3942.
2.—	3557.	3227.	2940.	2690.	2470.	2277.	2105.	1952.	1815.	1692.
3.—	1581.	1481.	1390.	1307.	1231.	1162.	1098.	1039.	985.4	935.5
4.—	889.3	846.5	806.6	769.5	735.0	702.7	672.4	644.1	617.6	592.6
5.—	569.2	547.1	526.2	506.5	488.0	470.4	453.7	437.9	423.0	408.8
6.—	395.2	382.4	370.2	358.5	347.4	336.8	326.7	317.0	307.7	298.9
7.—	290.4	282.3	274.5	267.0	259.8	253.0	246.3	240.0	233.9	228.0
8.—	222.3	216.9	211.6	206.5	201.7	196.9	192.4	188.0	183.7	179.6
9.—	175.7	171.8	168.1	164.5	161.0	157.7	154.4	151.2	148.2	145.2
10.—	142.3	139.5	136.8	134.1	131.6	129.1	126.6	124.3	122.0	119.8
11.—	117.6	115.5	113.4	111.4	109.5	107.6	105.7	103.9	102.2	100.5
12.—	98.81	97.19	95.60	94.05	92.54	91.07	89.63	88.22	86.85	85.51
13.—	84.20	82.91	81.66	80.44	79.24	78.07	76.93	75.81	74.72	73.65
14.—	72.60	71.57	70.57	69.58	68.62	67.68	66.75	65.85	64.96	64.09
15.—	63.24	62.40	61.59	60.78	60.00	59.23	58.47	57.73	57.00	56.28
16.—	55.58	54.89	54.22	53.55	52.90	52.26	51.64	51.02	50.41	49.82
17.—	49.24	48.66	48.10	47.54	47.00	46.46	45.94	45.42	44.91	44.41
18.—	43.92	43.43	42.96	42.49	42.03	41.57	41.13	40.69	40.26	39.83
19.—	39.42	39.00	38.60	38.20	37.81	37.42	37.04	36.66	36.29	35.93
20.—	35.57	35.22	34.87	34.53	34.19	33.86	33.53	33.21	32.89	32.57
21.—	32.27	31.96	31.66	31.36	31.07	30.78	30.50	30.22	29.94	29.67
22.—	29.40	29.13	28.87	28.61	28.36	28.11	27.86	27.61	27.37	27.13
23.—	26.90	26.67	26.44	26.21	25.99	25.77	25.55	25.33	25.12	24.91
24.—	24.70	24.50	24.30	24.10	23.90	23.71	23.51	23.32	23.14	22.95
25.—	22.77	22.59	22.41	22.23	22.05	21.88	21.71	21.54	21.38	21.21
26.—	21.05	20.89	20.73	20.57	20.42	20.26	20.11	19.96	19.81	19.66

Table 1 (Continued) Knoop hardness numbers for load of 1 gf

Diagonal of Indentation (Microns)	Knoop Hardness Number for Diagonal Measured to 0.1 Micron									
	.0	.1	.2	.3	.4	.5	.6	.7	.8	.9
27.—	19.52	19.37	19.23	19.09	18.95	18.82	18.68	18.54	18.41	18.28
28.—	18.15	18.02	17.89	17.77	17.64	17.52	17.40	17.27	17.15	17.04
29.—	16.92	16.80	16.69	16.57	16.46	16.35	16.24	16.13	16.02	15.92
30.—	15.81	15.71	15.60	15.50	15.40	15.30	15.20	15.10	15.00	14.90
31.—	14.81	14.71	14.62	14.52	14.43	14.34	14.25	14.16	14.07	13.98
32.—	13.90	13.81	13.72	13.64	13.55	13.47	13.39	13.31	13.23	13.15
33.—	13.07	12.99	12.91	12.83	12.75	12.68	12.60	12.53	12.45	12.38
34.—	12.31	12.24	12.17	12.09	12.02	11.95	11.89	11.82	11.75	11.68
35.—	11.62	11.55	11.48	11.42	11.35	11.29	11.23	11.16	11.10	11.04
36.—	10.98	10.92	10.86	10.80	10.74	10.68	10.62	10.56	10.51	10.45
37.—	10.39	10.34	10.28	10.23	10.17	10.12	10.06	10.01	9.958	9.906
38.—	9.854	9.802	9.751	9.700	9.650	9.600	9.550	9.501	9.452	9.403
39.—	9.355	9.307	9.260	9.213	9.166	9.120	9.074	9.028	8.983	8.938
40.—	8.893	8.849	8.805	8.761	8.718	8.675	8.632	8.590	8.548	8.506
41.—	8.465	8.423	8.383	8.342	8.302	8.262	8.222	8.183	8.144	8.105
42.—	8.066	8.028	7.990	7.952	7.915	7.878	7.841	7.804	7.768	7.731
43.—	7.695	7.660	7.624	7.589	7.554	7.520	7.485	7.451	7.417	7.383
44.—	7.350	7.316	7.283	7.250	7.218	7.185	7.153	7.121	7.090	7.058
45.—	7.027	6.996	6.965	6.934	6.903	6.873	6.843	6.813	6.783	6.754
46.—	6.724	6.695	6.666	6.638	6.609	6.581	6.552	6.524	6.497	6.469
47.—	6.441	6.414	6.387	6.360	6.333	6.306	6.280	6.254	6.228	6.202
48.—	6.176	6.150	6.125	6.099	6.074	6.049	6.024	6.000	5.975	5.951
49.—	5.926	5.902	5.878	5.854	5.831	5.807	5.784	5.761	5.737	5.714
50.—	5.692	5.669	5.646	5.624	5.602	5.579	5.557	5.536	5.514	5.492
51.—	5.471	5.449	5.428	5.407	5.386	5.365	5.344	5.323	5.303	5.282
52.—	5.262	5.242	5.222	5.202	5.182	5.162	5.143	5.123	5.104	5.085
53.—	5.065	5.046	5.027	5.009	4.990	4.971	4.953	4.934	4.916	4.898
54.—	4.880	4.862	4.844	4.826	4.808	4.790	4.773	4.756	4.738	4.721
55.—	4.704	4.687	4.670	4.653	4.636	4.619	4.603	4.586	4.570	4.554
56.—	4.537	4.521	4.505	4.489	4.473	4.457	4.442	4.426	4.410	4.395
57.—	4.379	4.364	4.349	4.334	4.319	4.304	4.289	4.274	4.259	4.244
58.—	4.230	4.215	4.201	4.186	4.172	4.158	4.144	4.129	4.115	4.102
59.—	4.088	4.074	4.060	4.046	4.033	4.019	4.006	3.992	3.979	3.966
60.—	3.952	3.939	3.926	3.913	3.900	3.887	3.875	3.862	3.849	3.837
61.—	3.824	3.811	3.799	3.787	3.774	3.762	3.750	3.738	3.726	3.714
62.—	3.702	3.690	3.678	3.666	3.654	3.643	3.631	3.619	3.608	3.596
63.—	3.585	3.574	3.562	3.551	3.540	3.529	3.518	3.507	3.496	3.485
64.—	3.474	3.463	3.452	3.442	3.431	3.420	3.410	3.399	3.389	3.378
65.—	3.368	3.357	3.347	3.337	3.327	3.317	3.306	3.296	3.286	3.276
66.—	3.267	3.257	3.247	3.237	3.227	3.218	3.208	3.198	3.189	3.179
67.—	3.170	3.160	3.151	3.142	3.132	3.123	3.114	3.105	3.095	3.086
68.—	3.077	3.068	3.059	3.050	3.041	3.032	3.024	3.015	3.006	2.997
69.—	2.989	2.980	2.971	2.963	2.954	2.946	2.937	2.929	2.921	2.912
70.—	2.904	2.896	2.887	2.879	2.871	2.863	2.855	2.847	2.839	2.831
71.—	2.823	2.815	2.807	2.799	2.791	2.783	2.776	2.768	2.760	2.752
72.—	2.745	2.737	2.730	2.722	2.715	2.707	2.700	2.692	2.685	2.677
73.—	2.670	2.663	2.656	2.648	2.641	2.634	2.627	2.620	2.613	2.605
74.—	2.598	2.591	2.584	2.577	2.571	2.564	2.557	2.550	2.543	2.536
75.—	2.530	2.523	2.516	2.509	2.503	2.496	2.490	2.483	2.476	2.470
76.—	2.463	2.457	2.451	2.444	2.438	2.431	2.425	2.419	2.412	2.406
77.—	2.400	2.394	2.387	2.381	2.375	2.369	2.363	2.357	2.351	2.345
78.—	2.339	2.333	2.327	2.321	2.315	2.309	2.303	2.297	2.292	2.286
79.—	2.280	2.274	2.268	2.263	2.257	2.251	2.246	2.240	2.234	2.229
80.—	2.223	2.218	2.212	2.207	2.201	2.196	2.190	2.185	2.179	2.174
81.—	2.169	2.163	2.158	2.153	2.147	2.142	2.137	2.132	2.127	2.121
82.—	2.116	2.111	2.106	2.101	2.096	2.091	2.086	2.080	2.075	2.070
83.—	2.065	2.060	2.056	2.051	2.046	2.041	2.036	2.031	2.026	2.021
84.—	2.017	2.012	2.007	2.002	1.998	1.993	1.988	1.983	1.979	1.974
85.—	1.969	1.965	1.960	1.956	1.951	1.946	1.942	1.937	1.933	1.928
86.—	1.924	1.919	1.915	1.911	1.906	1.902	1.897	1.893	1.889	1.884
87.—	1.880	1.876	1.871	1.867	1.863	1.858	1.854	1.850	1.846	1.842
88.—	1.837	1.833	1.829	1.825	1.821	1.817	1.813	1.809	1.804	1.800
89.—	1.796	1.792	1.788	1.784	1.780	1.776	1.772	1.768	1.765	1.761
90.—	1.757	1.753	1.749	1.745	1.741	1.737	1.733	1.730	1.726	1.722
91.—	1.718	1.715	1.711	1.707	1.703	1.700	1.696	1.692	1.688	1.685
92.—	1.681	1.677	1.674	1.670	1.667	1.663	1.659	1.656	1.652	1.649
93.—	1.645	1.642	1.638	1.635	1.631	1.628	1.624	1.621	1.617	1.614
94.—	1.610	1.607	1.604	1.600	1.597	1.593	1.590	1.587	1.583	1.580

Table 1 (Continued) Knoop hardness numbers for load of 1 gf

Diagonal of Indentation (Microns)	Knoop Hardness Number for Diagonal Measured to 0.1 Micron									
	.0	.1	.2	.3	.4	.5	.6	.7	.8	.9
95.—	1.577	1.573	1.570	1.567	1.563	1.560	1.557	1.554	1.550	1.547
96.—	1.544	1.541	1.538	1.534	1.531	1.528	1.525	1.522	1.519	1.515
97.—	1.512	1.509	1.506	1.503	1.500	1.497	1.494	1.491	1.488	1.485
98.—	1.482	1.479	1.476	1.473	1.470	1.467	1.464	1.461	1.458	1.455
99.—	1.452	1.449	1.446	1.443	1.440	1.437	1.434	1.431	1.429	1.426
100.—	1.423	1.420	1.417	1.414	1.412	1.409	1.406	1.403	1.400	1.398
101.—	1.395	1.392	1.389	1.387	1.384	1.381	1.378	1.376	1.373	1.370
102.—	1.368	1.365	1.362	1.360	1.357	1.354	1.352	1.349	1.346	1.344
103.—	1.341	1.339	1.336	1.333	1.331	1.328	1.326	1.323	1.321	1.318
104.—	1.316	1.313	1.311	1.308	1.305	1.303	1.301	1.298	1.296	1.293
105.—	1.291	1.288	1.286	1.283	1.281	1.278	1.276	1.274	1.271	1.269
106.—	1.266	1.264	1.262	1.259	1.257	1.255	1.252	1.250	1.247	1.245
107.—	1.243	1.240	1.238	1.236	1.234	1.231	1.229	1.227	1.224	1.222
108.—	1.220	1.218	1.215	1.213	1.211	1.209	1.206	1.204	1.202	1.200
109.—	1.198	1.195	1.193	1.191	1.189	1.187	1.185	1.182	1.180	1.178
110.—	1.176	1.174	1.172	1.170	1.167	1.165	1.163	1.161	1.159	1.157
111.—	1.155	1.153	1.151	1.149	1.147	1.145	1.142	1.140	1.138	1.136
112.—	1.134	1.132	1.130	1.128	1.126	1.124	1.122	1.120	1.118	1.116
113.—	1.114	1.112	1.110	1.108	1.106	1.105	1.103	1.101	1.099	1.097
114.—	1.095	1.093	1.091	1.089	1.087	1.085	1.083	1.082	1.080	1.078
115.—	1.076	1.074	1.072	1.070	1.068	1.067	1.065	1.063	1.061	1.059
116.—	1.057	1.056	1.054	1.052	1.050	1.048	1.047	1.045	1.043	1.041
117.—	1.039	1.038	1.036	1.034	1.032	1.031	1.029	1.027	1.025	1.024
118.—	1.022	1.020	1.018	1.017	1.015	1.013	1.012	1.010	1.008	1.006
119.—	1.005	1.003	1.001	0.9998	0.9981	0.9964	0.9947	0.9931	0.9914	0.9898
120.—	0.9881	0.9865	0.9848	0.9832	0.9816	0.9799	0.9783	0.9767	0.9751	0.9735
121.—	0.9719	0.9703	0.9687	0.9671	0.9655	0.9639	0.9623	0.9607	0.9591	0.9576
122.—	0.9560	0.9544	0.9529	0.9513	0.9498	0.9482	0.9467	0.9451	0.9436	0.9420
123.—	0.9405	0.9390	0.9375	0.9359	0.9344	0.9329	0.9314	0.9299	0.9284	0.9269
124.—	0.9254	0.9239	0.9224	0.9209	0.9195	0.9180	0.9165	0.9150	0.9136	0.9121
125.—	0.9107	0.9092	0.9078	0.9063	0.9049	0.9034	0.9020	0.9005	0.8991	0.8977
126.—	0.8963	0.8948	0.8934	0.8920	0.8906	0.8892	0.8878	0.8864	0.8850	0.8836
127.—	0.8822	0.8808	0.8794	0.8780	0.8767	0.8753	0.8739	0.8726	0.8712	0.8698
128.—	0.8685	0.8671	0.8658	0.8644	0.8631	0.8617	0.8604	0.8591	0.8577	0.8564
129.—	0.8551	0.8537	0.8524	0.8511	0.8498	0.8485	0.8472	0.8459	0.8446	0.8433
130.—	0.8420	0.8407	0.8394	0.8381	0.8368	0.8355	0.8343	0.8330	0.8317	0.8304
131.—	0.8291	0.8279	0.8266	0.8254	0.8241	0.8229	0.8216	0.8204	0.8191	0.8179
132.—	0.8166	0.8154	0.8142	0.8129	0.8117	0.8105	0.8093	0.8080	0.8068	0.8056
133.—	0.8044	0.8032	0.8020	0.8008	0.7996	0.7984	0.7972	0.7960	0.7948	0.7936
134.—	0.7924	0.7913	0.7901	0.7889	0.7877	0.7866	0.7854	0.7842	0.7831	0.7819
135.—	0.7807	0.7796	0.7784	0.7773	0.7761	0.7750	0.7738	0.7727	0.7716	0.7704
136.—	0.7693	0.7682	0.7670	0.7659	0.7648	0.7637	0.7626	0.7614	0.7603	0.7592
137.—	0.7581	0.7570	0.7559	0.7548	0.7537	0.7526	0.7515	0.7504	0.7493	0.7483
138.—	0.7472	0.7461	0.7450	0.7439	0.7429	0.7418	0.7407	0.7396	0.7386	0.7375
139.—	0.7365	0.7354	0.7343	0.7333	0.7322	0.7312	0.7301	0.7291	0.7281	0.7270
140.—	0.7260	0.7249	0.7239	0.7229	0.7218	0.7208	0.7198	0.7188	0.7177	0.7167
141.—	0.7157	0.7147	0.7137	0.7127	0.7117	0.7107	0.7097	0.7087	0.7077	0.7067
142.—	0.7057	0.7047	0.7037	0.7027	0.7017	0.7007	0.6997	0.6988	0.6978	0.6968
143.—	0.6958	0.6949	0.6939	0.6929	0.6920	0.6910	0.6900	0.6891	0.6881	0.6872
144.—	0.6862	0.6852	0.6843	0.6834	0.6824	0.6815	0.6805	0.6796	0.6786	0.6777
145.—	0.6768	0.6758	0.6749	0.6740	0.6731	0.6721	0.6712	0.6703	0.6694	0.6684
146.—	0.6675	0.6666	0.6657	0.6648	0.6639	0.6630	0.6621	0.6612	0.6603	0.6594
147.—	0.6585	0.6576	0.6567	0.6558	0.6549	0.6540	0.6531	0.6523	0.6514	0.6505
148.—	0.6496	0.6487	0.6479	0.6470	0.6461	0.6452	0.6444	0.6435	0.6426	0.6418
149.—	0.6409	0.6401	0.6392	0.6383	0.6375	0.6366	0.6358	0.6349	0.6341	0.6332
150.—	0.6324	0.6316	0.6307	0.6299	0.6290	0.6282	0.6274	0.6265	0.6257	0.6249
151.—	0.6241	0.6232	0.6224	0.6216	0.6208	0.6199	0.6191	0.6183	0.6175	0.6167
152.—	0.6159	0.6151	0.6143	0.6134	0.6126	0.6118	0.6110	0.6102	0.6094	0.6086
153.—	0.6078	0.6071	0.6063	0.6055	0.6047	0.6039	0.6031	0.6023	0.6015	0.6008
154.—	0.6000	0.5992	0.5984	0.5976	0.5969	0.5961	0.5953	0.5946	0.5938	0.5930
155.—	0.5923	0.5915	0.5907	0.5900	0.5892	0.5885	0.5877	0.5869	0.5862	0.5854
156.—	0.5847	0.5839	0.5832	0.5825	0.5817	0.5810	0.5802	0.5795	0.5787	0.5780
157.—	0.5773	0.5765	0.5758	0.5751	0.5743	0.5736	0.5729	0.5722	0.5714	0.5707
158.—	0.5700	0.5693	0.5685	0.5678	0.5671	0.5664	0.5657	0.5650	0.5643	0.5635
159.—	0.5628	0.5621	0.5614	0.5607	0.5600	0.5593	0.5586	0.5579	0.5572	0.5565
160.—	0.5558	0.5551	0.5544	0.5537	0.5531	0.5524	0.5517	0.5510	0.5503	0.5496
161.—	0.5489	0.5483	0.5476	0.5469	0.5462	0.5455	0.5449	0.5442	0.5435	0.5429
162.—	0.5422	0.5415	0.5408	0.5402	0.5395	0.5389	0.5382	0.5375	0.5369	0.5362

Table 1 (Continued) Knoop hardness numbers for load of 1 gf

Diagonal of Indentation (Microns)	Knoop Hardness Number for Diagonal Measured to 0.1 Micron									
	.0	.1	.2	.3	.4	.5	.6	.7	.8	.9
163.—	0.5356	0.5349	0.5342	0.5336	0.5329	0.5323	0.5316	0.5310	0.5303	0.5297
164.—	0.5290	0.5284	0.5278	0.5271	0.5265	0.5258	0.5252	0.5246	0.5239	0.5233
165.—	0.5226	0.5220	0.5214	0.5208	0.5201	0.5195	0.5189	0.5182	0.5176	0.5170
166.—	0.5164	0.5157	0.5151	0.5145	0.5139	0.5133	0.5127	0.5120	0.5114	0.5108
167.—	0.5102	0.5096	0.5090	0.5084	0.5078	0.5072	0.5066	0.5060	0.5054	0.5047
168.—	0.5041	0.5035	0.5030	0.5024	0.5018	0.5012	0.5006	0.5000	0.4994	0.4988
169.—	0.4982	0.4976	0.4970	0.4964	0.4959	0.4953	0.4947	0.4941	0.4935	0.4929
170.—	0.4924	0.4918	0.4912	0.4906	0.4900	0.4895	0.4889	0.4883	0.4878	0.4782
171.—	0.4866	0.4860	0.4855	0.4849	0.4843	0.4838	0.4832	0.4827	0.4821	0.4815
172.—	0.4810	0.4804	0.4799	0.4793	0.4787	0.4782	0.4776	0.4771	0.4765	0.4760
173.—	0.4754	0.4749	0.4743	0.4738	0.4732	0.4727	0.4721	0.4716	0.4711	0.4705
174.—	0.4700	0.4694	0.4689	0.4684	0.4678	0.4673	0.4668	0.4662	0.4657	0.4652
175.—	0.4646	0.4641	0.4636	0.4630	0.4625	0.4620	0.4615	0.4609	0.4604	0.4599
176.—	0.4594	0.4588	0.4583	0.4578	0.4573	0.4568	0.4562	0.4557	0.4552	0.4547
177.—	0.4542	0.4537	0.4532	0.4526	0.4521	0.4516	0.4511	0.4506	0.4501	0.4496
178.—	0.4491	0.4486	0.4481	0.4476	0.4471	0.4466	0.4461	0.4456	0.4451	0.4446
179.—	0.4441	0.4436	0.4431	0.4426	0.4421	0.4416	0.4411	0.4406	0.4401	0.4397
180.—	0.4392	0.4387	0.4382	0.4377	0.4372	0.4367	0.4363	0.4358	0.4353	0.4348
181.—	0.4343	0.4339	0.4334	0.4329	0.4324	0.4319	0.4315	0.4310	0.4305	0.4300
182.—	0.4296	0.4291	0.4286	0.4282	0.4277	0.4272	0.4268	0.4263	0.4258	0.4254
183.—	0.4249	0.4244	0.4240	0.4235	0.4230	0.4226	0.4221	0.4217	0.4212	0.4207
184.—	0.4203	0.4198	0.4194	0.4189	0.4185	0.4180	0.4176	0.4171	0.4167	0.4162
185.—	0.4158	0.4153	0.4149	0.4144	0.4140	0.4135	0.4131	0.4126	0.4122	0.4117
186.—	0.4113	0.4109	0.4104	0.4100	0.4095	0.4091	0.4087	0.4082	0.4078	0.4073
187.—	0.4069	0.4065	0.4060	0.4056	0.4052	0.4047	0.4043	0.4039	0.4034	0.4030
188.—	0.4026	0.4022	0.4017	0.4013	0.4009	0.4005	0.4000	0.3996	0.3992	0.3988
189.—	0.3983	0.3979	0.3975	0.3971	0.3967	0.3962	0.3958	0.3954	0.3950	0.3946
190.—	0.3942	0.3937	0.3933	0.3929	0.3925	0.3921	0.3917	0.3913	0.3909	0.3905
191.—	0.3900	0.3896	0.3892	0.3888	0.3884	0.3880	0.3876	0.3872	0.3868	0.3864
192.—	0.3860	0.3856	0.3852	0.3848	0.3844	0.3840	0.3836	0.3832	0.3828	0.3824
193.—	0.3820	0.3816	0.3812	0.3808	0.3804	0.3800	0.3796	0.3792	0.3789	0.3785
194.—	0.3781	0.3777	0.3773	0.3769	0.3765	0.3761	0.3757	0.3754	0.3750	0.3746
195.—	0.3742	0.3738	0.3734	0.3731	0.3727	0.3723	0.3719	0.3715	0.3712	0.3708
196.—	0.3704	0.3700	0.3695	0.3693	0.3689	0.3685	0.3681	0.3678	0.3674	0.3670
197.—	0.3666	0.3663	0.3659	0.3655	0.3652	0.3648	0.3644	0.3641	0.3637	0.3633
198.—	0.3630	0.3626	0.3622	0.3619	0.3615	0.3611	0.3608	0.3604	0.3600	0.3597
199.—	0.3593	0.3590	0.3586	0.3582	0.3579	0.3575	0.3572	0.3568	0.3564	0.3561
200.—	0.3557	0.3554	0.3550	0.3547	0.3543	0.3540	0.3536	0.3533	0.3529	0.3525

Source: MEI Course 12, "Mechanical Testing of Metals," Lesson 3, "Hardness Testing," ASM, 1983, p. 29-32

The hardness value for either Vickers or Knoop is a stress value and is expressed as kilograms per square millimeter. Thus, it is a very important mechanical property.

As in other types indentation hardness testing, a great deal of judgment is required in obtaining the optimum indentation size. When the indentation is obviously too small to obtain an accurate reading, the load should be increased. Conversely, if the indentation is unreasonably large, the load should be decreased.

When new materials are being tested, some experimentation with indenter loads is often required to obtain the optimum conditions. Once an acceptable practice has been established for a given material, load selection is no longer a problem.

Spacing of Indentations. The same guidelines used for spacing of indentations for Brinell and Rockwell testing are applicable to Vickers and Knoop microhardness testing. A typical sequence for performing a microhardness test is as follows:

- Place standard test block or sample in vise.

- Focus with low-power objective, adjust illumination.

- Focus with high-power objective, adjust illumination.

- Move mechanical stage to place area of interest at register point for indentation.

- Place desired load in position or dial load.

- Index to indenting position.

- Set times if electrically controlled, or with manual control use watch or timer.

- Actuate electrical start switch or mechanical latch.

- Remove load after time lapse (automatic if electrically controlled).

- Index to viewing position (usually high-power objective).

- Measure length of long diagonal (Knoop) or both diagonals (Vickers).

- Calculate hardness value (formula, calculator, or tables).

Hardness Number vs Load. Prior to the advent of the microhardness tester, it was assumed that the Vickers indenter (as well as other indenters giving geometrically similar indentations) produced a hardness number that was independent of the indenting load. This generally can be accepted for loads of approximately 1000 g and above. However, microhardness testing, when performed with loads of less than 500 g with the Knoop indenter and less than 100 g with the Vickers indenter, is a function of the magnitude of the test load. In most instances, microhardness values, particularly Knoop values, decrease with increasing load, as illustrated in Fig. 6.

When using very light loads, some observers have noticed an increase in microhardness values with increasing load (see curve identified as "Vickers" in Fig. 6). This is followed by a range in which the hardness becomes independent of the load and approaches a constant value (Fig. 6). This effect occurs with a wide range of materials, from those as soft as copper to fully hardened steel. Before these studies were made, most engineers felt that the Vickers hardness and the Knoop hardness, because of geometrically similar indentations, should be independent of the load.

Fig. 6 Relationship of hardness number and load for Knoop and Vickers indenters

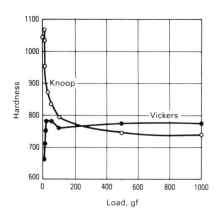

Load, gf

Source: **Metals Handbook, Mechanical Testing**, *Vol. 8, 9th ed., ASM, 1985, p. 96*

The apparent increase in hardness with decrease in load (in properly prepared surfaces) is primarily caused by (1) errors in the determination of the size of the indentation and (2) aberrations in the elastic recovery of the indentation. As the size of the indentation decreases, readings will be less accurate because of these factors. These inaccuracies may be related to the stress-strain curve of the material and to the relationship between the size of the indentation and the constituents of the workpiece material.

Other explanations of load dependence may be found in the design of the microhardness tester or in the testing procedure. Shape of the indenter, vibrations, microscope, friction within the tester, surface preparation and cold working, in addition to size of the indentation, elastic recovery, formation of a bulge, or other characteristics of the indentation itself, can affect the microhardness reading in varying ways, depending on the load.

In microhardness tests, it would seem likely that the load dependence is based to some extent on elastic recovery of the indentation after the load is removed. This is a factor with Knoop numbers, but experimental studies have indicated that elastic recovery of Vickers indentations is too small to explain load dependence completely. Another factor that must be considered is that the shape of the Vickers indentation often deviates from the square form. This is caused by the formation of a bulge at the sides of the indentation.

From a practical standpoint, however, load dependence is not as important as some may believe. The choice of load depends on the size and depth of indentation considered to be most desirable. Generally, the indentation is made as large as practicable to obtain the greatest accuracy possible. As long as a single load is used throughout a series of tests, the load dependence is of little significance. Using different loads in any particular investigation alters the as-measured hardness numbers; the lighter the load, the more significant the change. Generally, any comparison of Knoop hardness numbers with loads of less than 500 g and Vickers hardness numbers of less than 100 g is invalid, unless the load dependence is considered. This is the main reason for reporting the load when listing Knoop or Vickers numbers.

Specific Applications of Microhardness Testing

Microhardness testing is used extensively in research and for controlling quality of manufactured products. Testing of small workpieces, monitoring of surface-hardening processes, measuring the hardness of microconstituents, solving shop problems, and as a tool for use in failure analysis are among the principal uses of microhardness testing.

Testing of Small Workpieces. Many manufactured products, notably in the instrument and electronics industries, are too small to be tested for hardness by the more conventional methods. Many such workpieces can be tested without impairing their usefulness, generally by means of the holding and clamping fixtures shown in Fig. 5, or with holding fixtures specifically designed for the purpose. Often, such workpieces have a fine surface finish and do not need special preparation for testing. In other instances, at least a small area may need to be polished for use as a test spot.

Microhardness testing is also used on product forms that cannot be tested by other means. Thin foils and small-diameter wires are typical examples. Special preparation such as polishing may or may not be necessary, depending on the quality of the surface finish on the test workpiece. Fixtures such as those shown in Fig. 5(c), (d), and (e) usually are suitable for testing small or thin product forms. The minimum thickness of sheet or foil that can be tested depends on hardness and load, as shown in the Knoop minimum thickness chart in Fig. 7.

Fig. 7 Load and hardness combinations for determining minimum thickness of sheet or foil that can be tested on a Knoop hardness tester

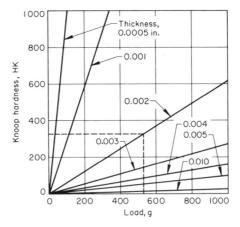

Assume that a maximum load value is needed for accurately testing a carbon steel workpiece 0.051 mm (0.002 in.) thick having an approximate hardness of 32 HRC. First, consult a conversion table for the equivalent Knoop hardness number (HK) of 32 HRC, which is 326 HK. Next, refer to the above chart at 326 HK and trace across to intersect at the 0.002-in. line, which is at about 525 g on the load line. Use the next lower standard load, which is 500 g
Source: Metals Handbook, Nondestructive Inspection and Quality Control, Vol. 11, 8th ed., ASM, 1976, p. 18

Monitoring of Surface-Hardening Processes. Microhardness testing is the best method for accurately determining case depth and various case conditions of carburized, carbonitrided, and nitrided workpieces, using the hardness survey procedure. In most instances, this is accomplished by use of test coupons that have accompanied the actual workpieces through the heat treating operation. The coupons then are sectioned and usually mounted for testing. To ensure accurate readings close to the edge of the cross section, the 100-g load is most frequently used, although a 500-g load is sometimes preferred. If the 100-g load is used, a metallographic finish is essential.

Readings are taken at pre-established intervals (commonly, 0.100 or 0.125 mm, 0.004 or 0.005 in.), usually beginning at least 0.025 mm (0.001 in.) from the edge of the workpiece. The results usually are plotted, as shown in Fig. 8(a). Note that the hardness of the carburized case is just over 800 HK at 0.025 mm (0.001 in.) from the surface; this hardness prevails for a depth of approximately 0.25 mm (0.010 in.), then gradually tapers off to the core hardness. The Knoop hardness readings are correlated with the indentations that increase in size as the metal becomes softer (Fig. 8a).

Fig. 8 Use of Knoop hardness for monitoring surface-hardening operations

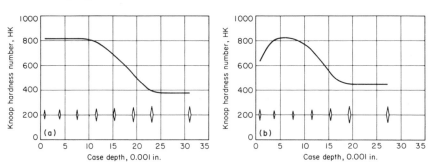

(a) Correlation of Knoop hardness readings with indentations on a cross section of a carburized case. (b) Similar to (a) except the effect of retained austenite (soft constituent) on the surface hardness is shown
Source: MEI Course 12, "Mechanical Testing of Metals," Lesson 3, "Hardness Testing," ASM, 1983, p. 37

Not only does this hardness survey show the case depth, but also shows the hardness at various depths and indicates about how much of the case can be safely removed in grinding or other finishing operations without impairing surface hardness. The survey also indicates that hardness at the surface is maximum, without signs of decarburization or retained austenite in the surface layer, both of which would make the layer soft.

The hardness survey shown in Fig. 8(b) indicates conditions different from those shown in Fig. 8(a), because the total case is thinner, core hardness is higher, and a relatively soft surface layer (0.102 mm, or 0.004 in. deep) is indicated. In the surface layer, the soft constituent proved to be retained austenite, although decarburization would have shown similarly on the hardness survey. Thus, about 0.100 mm (0.004 in.) should be removed in finishing to produce a surface of maximum hardness.

Measuring Hardness of Microconstituents. Figure 8(b) demonstrates how one microconstituent, in this instance retained austenite, can be detected by microhardness testing. Many metals are a mixture of microconstituents that vary widely in hardness. Ordinary hardness tests such as the Rockwell test result in an average reading that is less likely to show the true conditions.

A great deal can be learned about metals and their potential properties (for example, their resistance to wear) by knowing the actual hardness of their various microconstituents. Notable examples are the highly alloyed tool steels. Figure 9 shows a micrograph of polished and etched D2 tool steel. Knoop indentations taken on the matrix (darker constituent) and on the particles of complex alloy carbide (white) show an obvious variation in size. In this instance, the tests were made with a load of 50 g. The indentation on the matrix was 801 HK, whereas the carbide showed a value of 1930 HK. Actual Rockwell hardness on the C scale was 64 HRC (822 HK by conversion). Therefore, the Rockwell C scale did not register the true conditions.

Solving Shop Problems. Microhardness testing is often a useful tool in solving shop problems, notably those problems associated with cutting tools. A typical example is illustrated in Fig. 10. Cutting tools made from high speed steels, even though they have been correctly heat treated, frequently are damaged in grinding. Taps are among the most vulnerable, because the crests of teeth are thin and thus are likely to become overheated during grinding.

Fig. 9 Comparison of Knoop indentations in two microconstituents of quenched-and-tempered D2 tool steel

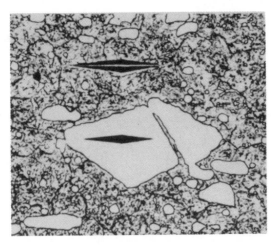

Indentation in a particle of chromium-vanadium carbide (white constituent) showed a value of 1930 HK, whereas the indentation in the matrix (darker constituent) was 801 HK. Both indentations were made with a 50-g load. Specimen was polished and etched in Vilella's reagent. 1000x.

Source: MEI Course 12, "Mechanical Testing of Metals," Lesson 3, "Hardness Testing," ASM, 1983, p. 38

In one instance, taps were failing prematurely from dulling of the tap teeth. Hardness measurements taken at various locations on the taps showed consistent values of 65 HRC, which was entirely acceptable. However, when one of the taps was sectioned and a tooth area was examined with a microhardness tester, results were quite different. Measurements taken at various locations with a Knoop indenter and a 100-g load showed readings of about 850 HK (by conversion, about 65 HRC) in the center of the tooth and to within 0.075 to 0.125 mm (0.003 to 0.005 in.) of the edge (see Fig. 10). At the very edge of the tooth crest, however, readings were as low as 480 HK, which converts to approximately 46 HRC. Variation in size of the indentations can be clearly seen in Fig. 10. Obviously, the softened condition was the result of abusive grinding practice and rendered the tap useless.

Use in Failure Analysis. Surface decarburization, retained austenite, damage from heat treating or grinding, and mixed compositions are all conditions that can be easily detected by investigations with a microhardness tester, but which may be overlooked by other techniques.

Fig. 10 Cross section of a tap tooth showing hardness variations caused by overheating during grinding

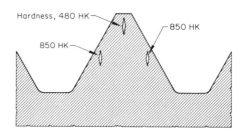

Source: MEI Course 12, "Mechanical Testing of Metals," Lesson 3, "Hardness Testing," ASM, 1983, p. 38

Interpretation of Hardness Test Results. Conversion of hardness test values among different scales for the same type of hardness tester, as well as conversion of results from one type of hardness tester to another, has always been controversial. Conversion tables developed by intensive research are readily available. Conversion from one scale to another can be directly applied only when the workpiece is consistent in hardness from the extreme surface layers to a depth of about ten times that of the indentation, for instance, with a workpiece of hardened and tempered shaft steel. A workpiece of this type that shows a hardness value of 327 HB (3000-kg load) will show an equivalent value of 35 HRC, or 68 HRA, or 37 HR45N. Furthermore, one can then predict with reasonable accuracy that the tensile strength (also shown on some conversion tables) of this workpiece will be about 157 ksi. Reasonably accurate conclusions relative to endurance limit and impact resistance can also be made from the hardness values.

Estimation of Case Depth. When a complexity of metallurgical conditions is involved, such as in carburizing or nitriding of workpiece surfaces, conversion tables must be used with extreme caution. The use of different hardness testing techniques can produce valuable information relative to the depth and character of the case or other surface conditions. Such information is most useful not only to determine where the case depth complies with specifications initially, but also to determine how much of the case has been or may be safely removed in finishing operations. For example, if a case hardened part is tested by a superficial Rockwell hardness tester and values of 91 HR15N, 79 HR30N, and 69 HR45N are obtained, and the test is continued by a regular Rockwell hardness tester and hardness values of 82.5 HRA and 62 HRC are obtained, certain conclusions can be drawn. Such results (within reasonable limits of error) indicate that the case is consistently hard and extends beyond a depth of 0.510 mm (0.020 in.) and probably farther, depending to some extent on the core hardness. If, on the other hand, the readings conformed to the conversion table until the Rockwell C reading was taken and were found low according to the conversion table, then it is obvious that the case is too thin to support the load used for the Rockwell C scale. Likewise, a decrease at any other point in such a line of readings will indicate a thinner case. Microhardness testing can play an important role in establishing precise case conditions.

Detection of Retained Austenite. Some carburizing steels, most notably those that have a high nickel content, are prone to the retention of austenite in the surface layers after hardening. This constituent is relatively soft and will show low readings from shallow indentations such as those made in Rockwell 15N tests. Such findings indicate, unless finishing operations are performed so that this constituent will be removed, that the heat treating operation may have to be revised to prevent formation of retained austenite. Microhardness tests are most useful in detection of retained austenite (see Fig. 8).

Detection of Decarburization. Surface decarburization, which can be one of the greatest detriments to achieving maximum mechanical properties of highly stressed parts, can also be detected by hardness testing, particularly by microhardness testing, because of the softness of decarburized surfaces. In many instances, a small amount of decarburization may be difficult to detect from the relatively deep indentation made by the Rockwell C tester, but will register readily on the scales for the superficial hardness tester.

A common application of hardness testing relative to surface decarburization is in the control of heat treating atmospheres and salt baths. This simple, but effective, technique involves the use of small test disks of a known steel, such as water-hardening tool steel (1% C). The test disk is heated in the furnace to be checked at the pre-established temperature and water-quenched. The test disk then is tested by means of both the Rockwell 15N and Rockwell C scale. If there is a lack of correlation (by the standard conversion table), it is quickly proved that surfaces are being adversely affected by the furnace atmosphere. Corrective measures then are applied before heat treating.

Limitations of Multiple-Indentation Testing. It should not be assumed that multiple-indentation testing, as described above, should be regularly used for routine testing. Neither should it be assumed that multiple-indentation testing can always replace more elaborate testing in a laboratory (as by microhardness testing). There are, however, many instances when laboratory facilities are not readily available, or when too much time is consumed for the more elaborate examinations.

Test procedure such as those described above should be applied only when general conditions are known and should be interpreted only by qualified personnel. However, when properly applied and interpreted, such tests can be helpful in process control and may often prevent needless rejection of valuable workpieces.

Chapter 6

Other Hardness Testing Methods

Scleroscope Hardness Testing

The Scleroscope hardness tester was the first commercially available metallurgical hardness tester produced in the United States. This instrument has been and still is used extensively for certain specific hardness testing applications.

The Scleroscope test consists of dropping a diamond-tipped hammer, which falls inside a glass tube under the force of its own weight from a fixed height, onto the test specimen and reading the rebound travel on a graduated scale. The height of the fall is 250 mm (10 in.). The hammer is a little less than 6 mm (0.25 in.) in diameter, 19 mm (0.75 in.) long, and weighs about 2 g (1/12 oz). The shape of the diamond is slightly spherical and blunt with a diameter of approximately 0.50 mm (0.020 in.).

The scale of rebound in the Scleroscope is arbitrarily chosen and consists of units, divided into 100 parts that represent the average rebound from pure, hardened, high-carbon steel. The scale is continued higher than 100 units to include metals that have greater hardnesses than fully hardened high-carbon steel. The value of 100 as the hardness number of hardened high-carbon steel was chosen as the most convenient.

The approximate relationships of Scleroscope hardness with Rockwell C and Brinell are presented in the Appendices.

Fig. 1 Model C-2 Scleroscope mounted in stand

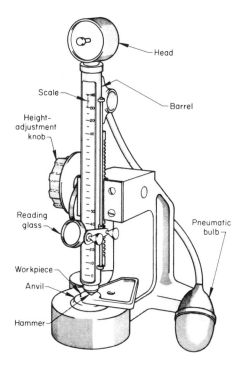

Source: **Metals Handbook, Mechanical Testing**, *Vol. 8, 9th ed., ASM, 1985, p. 105*

Scleroscope Testers. Scleroscope is a registered trademark of Shore Instrument and Manufacturing Co., Inc. Four commonly used types of Scleroscope hardness testers are shown in Fig. 1 through 5. The Model C-2 Scleroscope consists of a vertically disposed barrel containing a precision-bore glass tube. A base-mounted version of a Model C-2 Scleroscope is shown in Fig. 1. A scale, graduated from 0 to 140, is set behind the setup and is visible through the glass tube. Hardness is read from the vertical scale, usually with the aid of the reading glass attached to the tester. A pneumatic actuating head, affixed to the top of the barrel, is manually operated by a rubber bulb and tube. The hammer drops and rebounds with the glass tube.

A C-3 model of the Scleroscope is shown in Fig. 2. The principles of operation are essentially the same as for the C-2 model. The ability to transport the hardness tester to the workpiece is its principal advantage over other Scleroscope testers. Its height is only 250 mm (10 in.) and weight is 280 g (10 oz).

Fig. 2 Model C-3 Scleroscope

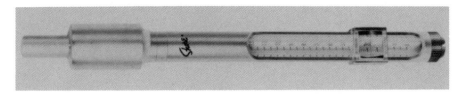

Courtesy of Shore Instrument and Manufacturing Co.

The Model D Scleroscope hardness tester (Fig. 3) is a dial-reading tester. The setup consists of a vertically disposed barrel that contains a clutch to arrest the hammer at maximum height of rebound. This is made possible because of the short rebound height. The hammer is longer and heavier than the hammer in the Model C Scleroscope and develops the same striking energy, although it drops a shorter distance.

Fig. 3 Principal components of the Model D Scleroscope hardness tester

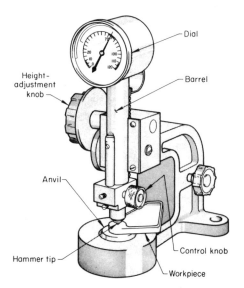

Source: ***Metals Handbook, Nondestructive Inspection and Quality Control****, Vol. 11, 8th ed., ASM, 1976, p. 14*

All models of the Scleroscope hardness tester may be mounted on various types of bases. The C-frame base, which rests on three points and is for bench use in hardness testing small workpieces, has a capacity about 75 mm (3 in.) high by 60 mm (2.5 in.) deep. A swing arm and post is also for bench use, but has height and reach capacities of 230 and 340 mm (9 and 14 in.), respectively. Another type of base is used for mounting the Scleroscope hardness tester on rolls and other cylindrical objects with minimum diameters of 2.5 in., or on flat, horizontal surfaces with minimum dimensions of 75 by 125 mm (3 by 5 in.).

Fig. 4 Model D Scleroscope dial

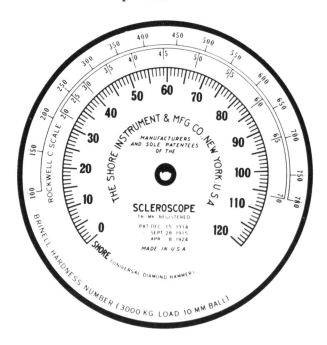

Courtesy of Shore Instrument and Manufacturing Co.

Models C-2 and C-3 commonly are used unmounted. However, when the hardness tester is unmounted, the workpiece should have a minimum weight of 2.3 kg (5 lb). The Model D Scleroscope hardness tester should not be used unmounted. The Model D instrument also has a dial that shows the approximate Scleroscope values converted to Rockwell C and Brinell (Fig. 4). A later addition to the line of available Scleroscope testers is the Electronic Digital Model D (Fig. 5).

The digital Scleroscope also operates on the rebound of a diamond tipped hammer dropped from a fixed height. The position of the diamond hammer at the apex of the rebound is sensed by a linear variable differential transducer and is transmitted to a digital indicator, reading directly in numbers of the Shore hardness scale.

Fig. 5 Digital readout Model D Scleroscope tester

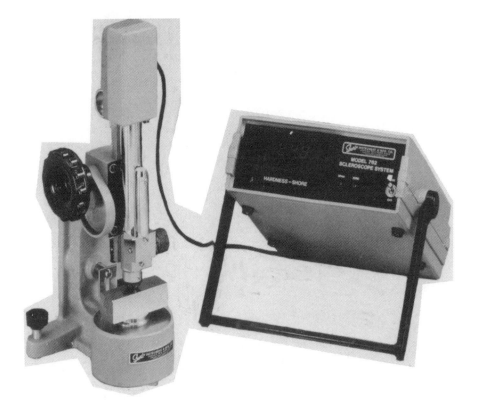

Courtesy of Shore Instrument and Manufacturing Co.

This instrument is capable of making more than 1000 tests/h. It can be used for testing a large variety of small parts when used with its clamping stand, as shown in Fig. 5. Tests on large items such as die blocks or crankshafts can be made by means of mounting on a roll test stand or swing arm. Freehand operation of this instrument is not recommended.

Workpiece Surface Finish Requirements. As with other metallurgical hardness testers, certain surface finish requirements on the workpiece must be met for Scleroscope hardness testing to make an accurate hardness determination. An excessively coarse surface finish will yield erratic readings. Hence, when necessary, the surface of the workpiece should be filed, machined, ground, or polished to permit accurate, consistent readings. Care should be taken to avoid overheating or excessively cold working the surface. The surface finish required to obtain reproducible results varies with the hardness of the workpiece. In proceeding from soft metals to hardened steel, the required surface finish ranges from a minimum finish, as produced by a No. 2 file, to a finely ground or polished finish.

Limitations on Workpiece Thickness. Case hardened steels with cases as thin as 0.250 mm (0.010 in.) can be accurately hardness tested, provided the core hardness is no less than 30 Scleroscope. Softer cores require a minimum case thickness of 0.380 mm (0.015 in.) for accurate results.

Thin strip or sheet may be tested, with some limitations, but only when the Scleroscope hardness tester is mounted in the clamping stand. Ideally, the sheet should be flat and without undulation. If the sheet material is bowed, the concave side should be placed up to preclude any possibility of erroneous readings due to spring effect. The minimum thicknesses of sheet in various categories that may be hardness tested are as follows:

Hardened steel	0.005 in.
Cold finished steel strip	0.010 in.
Annealed brass strip	0.010 in.
Half-hard brass strip	0.010 in.

Test Procedure

To perform a hardness test with either the Model C-2, Model C-3, or the Model D Scleroscope hardness tester, the tester should be held or set in a vertical position, with the bottom of the barrel in firm contact with the workpiece. The hammer is raised to the elevated position and then allowed to fall and strike the surface of the workpiece. The height of rebound, which indicates hardness, is then measured. When using the Model C-2 Scleroscope hardness tester, the hammer is raised to the elevated position by squeezing the pneumatic bulb. The hammer is released by again squeezing the bulb. When using the Model D Scleroscope hardness tester, the hammer is raised to the elevated position by turning the knurled control knob clockwise until a definite stop is reached. The hammer is allowed to strike the workpiece by releasing the control knob. The reading is recorded on the dial.

To minimize errors, the hardness tester must be set or held in a vertical position, using the plumb rod or level on the hardness tester to determine vertical alignment. The most accurate readings are obtained with the Scleroscope hardness tester mounted in a C-frame base that rests on three points, two of which are adjustable to facilitate leveling of the anvil and to ensure vertical alignment of the barrel. The opposite sides of the workpiece being hardness tested in a mounted tester must be parallel with each other. Vibrations must be avoided, because they impede free fall of the hammer, thereby producing low readings.

As is true for other methods of indentation hardness testing, spacing of indentations and proximity of the indentations with reference to edges of the test material is quite important. Indentations should be at least 0.50 mm (0.020 in.) apart and only one at the same spot. Flat workpieces with parallel surfaces may be hardness tested within 6 mm (0.25 in.) of the edge when properly clamped.

Taking the Readings. Some experience is necessary to accurately interpret the hardness readings on a Model C-2 and Model C-3 Scleroscope hardness testers. Thin materials or those weighing less than 2.3 kg (5 lb) must be securely clamped to absorb the inertia of the hammer. The sound of the impact is an indication of the effectiveness of the clamping; a dull thud indicates that the workpiece has been clamped solid, whereas a hollow ringing sound indicates that the workpiece is not tightly clamped, or is warped and not properly supported. Five hardness determinations should be made and their average taken as representative of the hardness of a particular workpiece.

Furthermore, in using the Model C-2 and Model C-3 testers, accurate readings depend upon eye "catching" the rebound height of the diamond-tipped hammer. Even with the aid of the reading glass shown in Fig. 1 and 2, there is the possibility of some disagreement among different operators. This is especially true when the instrument is used as a portable tester without being held in the C-frame. Under these conditions, there may be some difference in the readings, depending on how nearly vertical the instrument is held. The chances of discrepancy is less when using the Model D tester compared with the Model C-2 and Model C-3 testers for two reasons: (1) the Model D tester is never unmounted; and (2) readings are presented on a dial.

Calibration. Scleroscope hardness testers are supplied with reference bars (or test blocks) of known hardness to check the accuracy of the instrument. The reference bars can be used properly only with a mounted Scleroscope hardness tester, because the reference bars do not have sufficient mass to produce a full rebound of the hammer unless firmly clamped. If the reference bars are not clamped, the readings obtained will be low and erratic. If the Scleroscope readings do not check with the values of the reference bars, the hardness tester should be returned to the manufacturer for service.

Advantages and Limitations. A major advantage of the Scleroscope tester is portability. Although it is always preferable to use the C Model in the C-frame, it can be used (with care) without mounting, which expands its useful range. Without the frame, the Model C-2 and Model C-3 testers can be carried around the shop easily in the pocket of a conventional shop coat. Typical applications are in tool rooms, where the Scleroscope can be used to check hardness in strategic locations of various tools, as well as for inspecting localized conditions of grinding burn or decarburization because of its extreme sensitivity to shallow surface conditions.

In one plant, a Scleroscope was used constantly to monitor hardness of ground surfaces on the hardened bearings of high-performance crankshafts. Skillful use of a Scleroscope easily detected soft spots inflicted by overheating during grinding.

Other advantages of the Scleroscope hardness test include:

- Tests can be made very rapidly--over 100 tests/h are possible.

- Operation is simple and does not require highly skilled technicians.

- Scleroscope hardness testing is a nonmarring test procedure; craters are not created, and only in the most unusual instances would the tiny hammer mark be objectionable on a finished workpiece.

- A single scale accommodates the complete hardness range from the softest to the hardest metals.

The Scleroscope test is also subject to the following limitations: The hardness tester should be in a vertical position, or the free fall of the hammer will be impeded and result in erratic readings. Scleroscope hardness tests are more sensitive to variations in surface conditions than some other hardness tests. Finally, because readings taken with the C Models are those observed from the maximum rebound of the hammer on the first bounce, even the most experienced operators may disagree among themselves by 1 or 2 points in the reading.

Ultrasonic Microhardness Testing

Ultrasonic microhardness testing offers a new innovation in microhardness testing compared to the more conventional methods that are based on visual (microscopic) evaluation of an indentation after the load has been removed. Ultrasonic testing uses a maximum indentation load of approximately 800 gf. Therefore, as in other microhardness techniques, the indentation depth is relatively small (from 4 to 18 microns). In the vast majority of instances, the workpiece surface is unharmed, thus classifying this test as nondestructive. Measured values in either the Vickers or Rockwell C scale are displayed on a digital readout display directly after penetration of the test piece. This feature renders the method suitable for automated on-line testing. Up to 1200 parts/h can be tested. Table 1 compares various aspects of indentation-type hardness testing techniques, including the ultrasonic method.

In ultrasonic microhardness testing, a Vickers diamond is attached to one end of a magnetostrictive metal rod. The diamond-tipped rod is excited to its natural frequency by a piezoelectric converter. The resonant frequency of the rod changes as the free end of the rod is brought into contact with the surface of a solid body.

Table 1 Comparison of indentation hardness tests

Test	Indenter(s)	Indent — Diagonal or diameter	Indent — Depth	Load(s)	Method of measurement	Surface preparation	Tests per hour	Applications	Remarks
Brinell	Ball indenter, 10 mm or 2.5 mm in diameter	1-7 mm	Up to 0.3 mm and 1 mm, respectively, with 2.5-mm and 10-mm-diam balls	3000 kgf for ferrous materials down to 100 kgf for soft metals	Measure diameter of indentation under microscope; read hardness from tables	Specially ground area for measurements of diameter	50 with diameter measurements	Large forged and cast parts	Damage to specimen minimized by use of lightly loaded ball indenter. Indent then less than Rockwell
Rockwell	120° diamond cone, 1/16- to 1/2-in.-diam ball	0.1-1.5 mm	25-375 μm	Major 60-150 kgf Minor 10 kgf	Read hardness directly from meter or digital display	No preparation necessary on many surfaces	300 manually 900 automatically	Forgings, castings, roughly machined parts	Measure depth of penetration, not diameter
Rockwell superficial	As for Rockwell	0.1-0.7 mm	10-110 μm	Major 15-45 kgf Minor 3 kgf	As for Rockwell	Machined surface, ground	As for Rockwell	Critical surfaces of finished parts	A surface test of case hardening and annealing
Vickers	136° diamond pyramid	Measure diagonal, not diameter	0.03-0.1 mm	1-120 kgf	Measure indent with low-power microscope; read hardness from tables	Smooth clean surface, symmetrical if not flat	Up to 180	Fine finished surfaces, thin specimens	Small indent but high local stresses
Microhardness	136° diamond indenter or a Knoop indenter	40 μm	1-4 μm minimum	1 gf-1 kgf	Measure indentation with low-power microscope; read hardness from tables	Polished surface	Up to 60	Surface layers, thin stock down to 200 μm	Laboratory test used on brittle materials or microstructural constituents
Ultrasonic	136° diamond pyramid	15-50 μm	4-18 μm	800 gf	Direct readout onto meter or digital display	Surface better than 1.2 μm for accurate work. Otherwise, up to 3 μm	1200 (limited by speed at which operator can read display)	Thin stock and finished surfaces in any position	Calibration for Young's modulus necessary. 100% testing of finished parts. Completely nondestructive

The minimum material thickness for a test usually is taken to be ten times the indentation depth
Source: Metals Handbook, Mechanical Testing, Vol. 8, 9th ed., ASM, 1985, p. 102

Once the device is calibrated for the known modulus of elasticity of the tested material, the area of contact between the diamond tip and the tested surface can be derived from the measured resonant frequency. The area of contact is inversely proportional to the hardness of the tested material, provided the force pressing the surface is constant. Consequently, the measured frequency value can be converted into the corresponding hardness number.

Components of an ultrasonic hardness tester, which automatically bring the diamond-tipped oscillating rod into contact with the test piece and electronically perform all necessary measurements and calculations, are shown schematically in Fig. 6. The hardness number is displayed on a digital readout, while the oscillating rod is retracted to protect it until the next reading. The entire process generally takes less than 15 s.

This type of instrument is quite small and is battery powered for portability. The automatic probe allows hardness measurements to be made in any orientation, further enhancing its usefulness.

Fig. 6 Components of an ultrasonic hardness tester

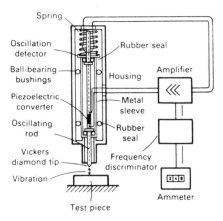

*Source: **Metals Handbook, Mechanical Testing**, Vol. 8, 9th ed., ASM, 1985, p. 101*

Fig. 7 Setup used for ultrasonic hardness tests

Courtesy of Krautkramer Branson

Setups for Specific Testing Conditions. A typical setup for taking hardness reading with an ultrasonic instrument is shown in Fig. 7. Note the "black box," or control instrument, and the indenter and related components mounted in a fixture. Figure 7 represents ultrasonic hardness testing under ideal conditions, but the instrument is quite flexible, and by means of a probe and suitably designed fixtures for holding the probe, the possibilities are virtually unlimited. A unique fixture for testing thin sheet metal is illustrated in Fig. 8.

Fig. 8 Specialized probe-fixture arrangement for testing thin pieces of sheet metal

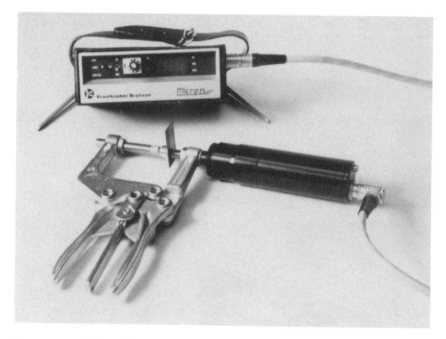

Courtesy of Krautkramer Branson

Figure 9 shows the test point, fixture, and actual testing of fillet radii on an engine crankshaft. In this instance, it was possible to take 10 readings/min. The technique and fixtures for testing profiles on gear teeth made from case hardened steel are shown in Fig. 10. With this technique, it was possible to take 8 readings/min.

Various types of probes are available, but one popular type has a round, flat end and can be hand held. This type of instrument is most frequently used on flat workpieces. In one specific instance, a die casting plant was having trouble with heat checking of dies. The dies were made from H13 tool steel quenched and tempered. On-site hardness tests with an ultrasonic instrument proved that the superficial surface was quite soft as a result of decarburization, even though Rockwell C readings (actual) were acceptable. The decarburized layer was thus the cause of heat checking, and corrective measures were applied to the heat treating procedure.

Fig. 9 Ultrasonic hardness testing application

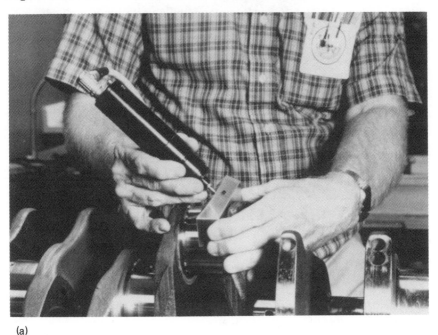

(a)

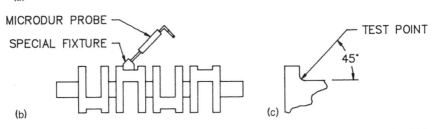

(a) Hardness testing of fillet radius on an engine crankshaft. (b) Probe and special fixture. (c) Test location
Courtesy of Krautkramer Branson

Fig. 10 Ultrasonic hardness testing application

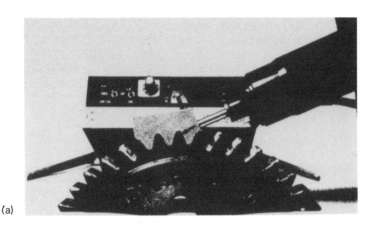

(a)

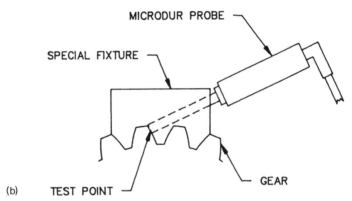

(b)

(a) Ultrasonic hardness testing of gear tooth flanks. (b) Schematic of probe, special fixture and test point
Courtesy of Krautkramer Branson

Capabilities of Ultrasonic Microhardness Testing

There are several outstanding advantages of the ultrasonic hardness testing system. Primarily, there is less chance of error because of the different conditions under which the indentation is measured. With an ultrasonic hardness testing system, it is possible to measure instantly the area of indentation under load. In principle, this ability is indispensable, because hardness numbers are derived by dividing the load by the surface area of the indentation. In conventional microhardness tests, this area is calculated from microscopic measurements of the lengths of the diagonals of the impression. However, using this method of indentation area measurement can lead to erroneous hardness values due to elastic recovery on unloading.

For example, a perfect indentation made with a perfect Vickers indenter would be a square (Fig. 11a). However, anomalies frequently are observed with a pyramid indenter. The pincushion indentation in Fig. 11(b) is the result of sinking-in of the metal around the flat faces of the pyramid. This condition is observed with annealed metals and results in an overestimate of the diagonal length. The barrel-shaped indentation in Fig. 11(c) is found in cold worked metals. It results from ridging or piling up of the metal around the faces of the indenter. The diagonal measurement in this case produces a low value of the contact area, so that the hardness numbers are erroneously high. Because the area of the indentation is measured under load in ultrasonic hardness testing, elastic recovery does not affect results.

Fig. 11 Distortion of diamond pyramid indentations due to elastic effects

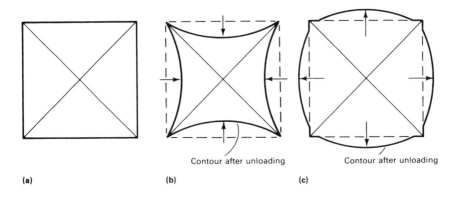

Contour after unloading   Contour after unloading

(a)   (b)   (c)

(a) Perfect indentation. (b) Pincushion indentation caused by material sinking in around the flat faces of the pyramid. (c) Barreled indentation caused by ridging of the material around the faces of the indenter
*Source: **Metals Handbook, Mechanical Testing**, Vol. 8, 9th ed., ASM, 1985, p. 102*

The advantage described above is further exemplified by Fig. 12. Whereas procedures based on the measurement of diagonals would provide the same measurement for all three indentation geometries shown, ultrasonic measurement would result in three different values.

Fig. 12 Indentations with equal diameters but different areas

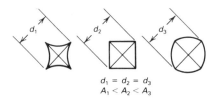

$$d_1 = d_2 = d_3$$
$$A_1 < A_2 < A_3$$

*Source: **Metals Handbook, Mechanical Testing**, Vol. 8, 9th ed., ASM, 1985, p. 102*

As in conventional Vickers and Brinell hardness testing, a single loading force is utilized. Thus, in ultrasonic hardness testing, no time is lost in consecutive load application as in Rockwell testing. Because only one test load is used in ultrasonic testing, sensitive displacement-measuring instruments are not necessary, and rigid machine frames are not required. In many instances, it is possible to perform the hardness measurement with ultrasonic testing without clamping or rigidly supporting the test material, which simplifies design and handling.

Because the sensitivity and resolving power of the ultrasonic instrument can be increased to high levels, it is possible to measure even the smallest indentation. Hardness profile curves can be obtained by untrained personnel automatically in a fraction of the time previously required. The digital display virtually eliminates operator interpretation errors. A memory feature, which will hold the last reading displayed for up to 3 min or until another reading is taken, facilitates any manual recording of data that is necessary.

A one-point calibration procedure allows the instrument to be set up quickly and easily. The few controls and adjustments that are required, coupled with a motor-driven probe, facilitate repeatable test results. The portability of ultrasonic microhardness testers allows hardness evaluations to be taken not only in a laboratory environment, but also on-site, in the field, and in any specimen orientation. Inspection of large parts and on-line in-process inspection hardness testing is possible.

Typical applications of ultrasonic microhardness testing are in the automotive, nuclear, petrochemical, aerospace, and machinery manufacturing industries, including finished goods with hardened surfaces, thin case hardened parts, thin sheet, strip, coils, platings, and coatings. Often, 100% inspection is possible on critically stressed components. Small components and difficult-to-access parts can also be tested by the ultrasonic microhardness method, either in a hand-held or a fixtured mode.

Portability is one of the important advantages of ultrasonic microhardness testers. The entire assembly fits into a convenient carrying case so that it can be easily hand carried. It is, by far, the most portable microhardness tester, and even approaches the Scleroscope in degree of portability. While it is preferable to hold the element in a fixture and test on a flat surface, there are numerous other positions in which it can be used with a wide variety of fixtures, or by hand with the probe. Thus, this type of instrument is not only a laboratory instrument, but can also be used as an on-site inspection tool.

Limitations of Ultrasonic Microhardness Testing

The principal disadvantage of the ultrasonic technique is the characteristic that is, in many cases, an advantage--is the lack of an optical system. Reading the indentations by an optical system is slow and tedious, but it does permit precise location of the indenter in relation to locations on the test metal. With the ultrasonic system, obtaining readings on microconstituents becomes difficult, because there is no way to precisely spot the indenter.

This characteristic of ultrasonic testing is, in many instances, a drawback in making hardness traverses on case hardened steels. With the conventional Vickers or Knoop systems, common practice is to position the test piece, so that the first indentation is made at some prescribed distance from the edge, such as 0.05 or 0.10 mm (0.002 or 0.004 in.), for example, and then make a series of indentations at established intervals for the distance required to determine the depth of hard case. However, with ultrasonic instruments, positioning the indenter to obtain a near-the-edge reading is very difficult.

This difficulty can be overcome by taking the first reading at an appreciable distance from the edge (beyond the point at which the case exists), then working outward at prescribed intervals toward the edge, until a very soft reading occurs, thus indicating that the indenter has reached the softer mounting material.

Surface Finish Requirements. Regardless of other variations, ultrasonic testing actually constitutes microhardness testing, and as such, the surface finish of the test material must be taken into account. To accurately measure any Vickers (diamond pyramid) indentation, it must be clearly defined. Therefore, requirements for surface finish are stringent. These requirements become increasingly stringent as the load decreases. Therefore, to accommodate the force used in ultrasonic testing, a metallographic finish is required. When grinding, polishing, or both operations are necessary for specimen preparation, care should be taken to minimize heating and distortion of the specimen surface. Polishing should be performed according to the procedures outlined in ASTM E3, "Standard Methods for Preparation of Metallographic Specimens."

When the specimen to be tested for microhardness will also be used for metallographic examination, mounting (usually in plastic) and polishing are justified. In other instances, only polishing is required.

When mounting is not necessary, fixtures may be used for holding the specimens or workpieces. Typical fixture arrangements are shown in Fig. 5 in Chapter 5. Most workpieces can be adapted to any one of the commonly used fixture types. Fixtures must maintain a rigid surface perpendicular to the indenter. The holding and polishing vise shown in Fig. 5 in Chapter 5 can reduce preparation time, because the specimen can be polished and tested without removing it from the vise. The turntable vise fixture shown in Fig. 5 in Chapter 5 is convenient for holding mounted specimens.

When ultrasonic readings are taken in the shop on actual workpieces, some means of obtaining a good surface finish must be used. This usually can be accomplished by metallographic emery papers. As a rule, it is desirable to avoid stock removal on actual parts that are scheduled to undergo hardness testing.

Scratch and File Testing

Scratch Test. The Mohs scale of hardness, developed primarily for evaluating hardness of minerals, has been in use since 1922. This scale consists of ten minerals arranged in order from 1 to 10. Diamond is rated as the hardest and is indexed as 10. Talc is the softest with an index number of 1. Each mineral in the scale will scratch all those below it as follows:

Diamond	10
Corundum	9
Topaz	8
Quartz	7
Orthoclase (Feldspar)	6
Apatite	5
Fluorite	4
Calcite	3
Gypsum	2
Talc	1

The steps between the above numbers are not, however, of equal value. The difference in hardness, for example, between 9 and 10 is much greater than between 1 and 2. To determine the hardness of a mineral, it is necessary to determine which of the standard materials the unknown will scratch; the hardness will lie between two points on the scale--the point between the mineral that may be scratched and the next harder one. It is an exact quantitative test, however, and the standards are purely arbitrary numbers.

Although the materials engineer and metallurgist find little use of the Mohs scale, the hardness of several common metals and alloys is as follows: "Armco" iron is between 3 and 4, copper is between 2 and 3, and hardened tool steel is between 7 and 8.

At least two instruments have been designed for quantitatively measuring hardness by the scratch method. One instrument was intended to overcome the disadvantages of the Mohs scale in that the measurements would eliminate the personal judgment factor, and the overlapping of the hardness ranges of various minerals was greatly reduced. The instrument consisted primarily of a microscope, stage, sliding weight to apply loads to 3 g, and a diamond point. The diamond was ground to a semicircular, blade-like edge with a 45° included angle. In operation, the mineral being tested is scratched by the diamond, and the scratch is compared with standard limit scratches in the microscope eyepiece. The load is adjusted, and additional scratches are made until a scratch is produced within the standard limits. Usually, this is accomplished in three trials. The scale is based on the actual weight on the testing point in grams. This instrument is no longer used commercially.

Another scratch test unit is available as an accessory to the Tukon hardness tester. Either the Knoop or the Vickers indenters may be used. Movement of the specimen during the scratch period is controlled by dead weight and an oil-filled dash pot. Loads of 1, 2, 5, 10, and 25 g can be used, and all are placed on the indenter screw directly over the indenter. The length of scratch is approximately 100 microns. The speed of the specimen under the indenter is adjustable, but should be between 0.044 and 0.066 mm/min. All operations of this test--lowering indenter, moving the specimen to make the scratch, and finally lifting the indenter from the specimen--are mechanically controlled. The possibility of erroneous results from nonuniform action (manual operation can never be as uniform as mechanical operation) are practically eliminated.

File testing was developed by applying a similar principle to hardness testing as used in the scratch test. The file test is useful in estimating the hardness of steels in the high hardness ranges. It provides information on soft spots and decarburization quickly and easily. Standard test files are heat treated to approximately 67 to 70 HRC. The flat portion of the file is pressed firmly against, and slowly drawn across, the surface to be tested. If the file does not bite, the material is designated "file hard."

The results of the test are influenced by a number of factors such as pressure, speed, angle of contact, and surface roughness. Consequently, its ability to yield reproducible hardness values is rather limited, and reasonable accuracy is obtained only at the highest hardness levels. In such instances, the file test is quite useful for detecting soft spots or decarburization (loss of carbon from the surface layers), particularly on odd shapes and sizes that are difficult to test by other methods.

Thin, hard surface layers produced by special heat treating procedures such as cyaniding or nitriding also might require file testing, if other hardness testers tend to penetrate the case. Files can be tempered from their original hardness of 67 to 70 HRC to various lower degrees of hardness, ground to a point, and used to determine the scratch hardness of quenched-and-tempered products. However, such an application of the file test has limited usefulness.

Any appreciable degree of accuracy in file testing necessarily depends on operator skill, which is obtained through extensive of practice with standards of known hardness. In general, the edge of a test file should not be used, as this practice may "tear" a very hard metal. Excessive pressure on the file should also be avoided, because it may result in an erroneous interpretation.

Evaluation of Hardness by Eddy Current Testing

Eddy current testing is based on electrical principles rather than on a mechanical principle. Not unlike many other procedures used in the metals industry, eddy-current testing measures one property that is directly related to another specific property. For example, temperatures inside heat treating furnaces are measured indirectly by the change in emf values of two dissimilar metals (thermocouples). These changes are then converted to changes in temperature. Another example is the indirect measurement of heat treating furnace atmospheres. Carbon potential usually is controlled by controlling dew point or oxygen content rather than by direct measurement of carbon.

In eddy-current testing, current is induced to flow into a workpiece by means of a primary coil. This may be accomplished by having the primary coil encircle the workpiece, although a probe also may be used. Changes registered in the current caused by variations in characteristics of the workpiece thus offer a means of evaluating workpiece variables. Therefore, the eddy current method does not measure hardness *per se* as in indentation testing methods. Instead, hardness is measured indirectly by measuring a related characteristic, and comparing this value to a known standard.

Eddy-current testing covers a wide range of applications including location of defects and sorting of metal parts for variations in composition, hardness, grain size, and case depth. A principal use of eddy-current testing is for locating seams and other imperfections in mill products (primarily bars and tubes) on a mass-production basis. This inspection method may be applied to either ferrous or nonferrous metals, although the approaches for each are vastly different. High current frequencies are required for examining nonferrous metals. During sorting of nonferrous metals for composition, variations in conductivity of the work metal are used to indicate variations in composition.

Electromagnetic Testing

Electromagnetic testing is one type of eddy-current testing, and it is most frequently used to sort ferrous metal workpieces. In a typical application small steel parts were made from T1 high speed tool steel and hardened by air cooling from 1260 °C (2300 °F). Unfortunately, a mix up in the steel stockroom allowed some parts to be made from W1 tool steel (a simple, high-carbon grade). The W1 parts were essentially ruined after subjection to the air cooling treatment, but after centerless grinding, all parts looked the same.

The problem of sorting the parts was solved by electromagnetic testing, using one reference coil and one coil for the unknown. Even by manual operation, it was possible to test (nondestructively) at the rate of about 6000 parts/h. An automated setup was then developed that permitted testing of 12,000 parts/h. This setup was equipped with a device that immediately shut the instrument down when a W1 part appeared.

The above test was adopted for testing all such parts to prevent any defective parts being put into service, which may have had detrimental effects. In the procedure described above, a variation in magnetic permeability was the basis of sorting.

Equipment for Electromagnetic Testing. A typical electromagnetic setup is illustrated in Fig. 13. This new Verimet (one of the many units commonly referred to as "black boxes") combines high field strength and precise analysis of first, third, and fifth harmonic eddy-current signals. It is capable of sorting heat treated parts for any one of several variables including hardness. Note the twin coils on the right, one of which is used to surround the reference part, or standard, whereas the other coil surrounds the part to be tested. The instrument shown in Fig. 13 is a 60-Hz base frequency, 60-Hz, 115-V AC comparator. This model is equipped with a built-in oscilloscope readout, but a similar instrument is available with a meter display.

Fig. 13 Instrumentation setup for the "Harmonic Comparator"

The comparator is used to evaluate hardness and other variables in metal products
Courtesy of K.J. Law Engineers, Inc.

Specific Applications. The electromagnetic test, as previously stated, is not a hardness test *per se*, but can be used for sorting ferrous metal parts on the basis of some other characteristic, which, in turn, can be used to measure hardness. Sorting is accomplished by use of reference coils that are initially balanced with sample parts of known hardness. Parts of unknown hardness then are substituted for one of the reference parts. The degree of unbalance that results then is correlated with differences in hardness.

Readout is most often done with an oscilloscope. Figure 14 illustrates examples of luminous point patterns representing three ranges of hardness. These patterns were developed in connection with sorting mixed lots of steel studs. The required hardness range established for these hardened and tempered studs was 35 to 40 HRC. However, some studs were in a higher range of hardness, because they were not tempered, whereas others fell short because of surface decarburization. These mixed lots were sorted successfully into three hardness ranges based on oscilloscope point patterns as shown in Fig.

14. Another application for sorting hardened steel parts for hardness variations of 1 to 2 points HRC is shown in Fig. 15.

Fig. 14 Luminous point patterns representing three ranges of hardness

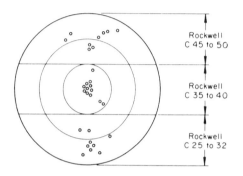

The patterns, as they appeared on an oscilloscope, were used in sorting mixed lots of tapered studs on the basis of hardness
Source: MEI Course 12, "Mechanical Testing of Metals," Lesson 3, "Hardness Testing," ASM, 1983, p. 38

Limitations of Eddy Current Testing for Hardness. Electromagnetic systems frequently can be used advantageously for sorting on the basis of hardness. Such testing is conducted more quickly than any other testing procedure. However, there are definite limitations to this method:

- As a rule, workpieces must be identical to one another in size and shape.

- Setups are expensive, so that they can rarely be justified unless many identical parts (usually many thousands) are involved.

- Reference parts of known hardness are essential. Furthermore, it must be ascertained that hardness is the only significant variable. If there are other significant variables, such as composition or microstructure as well as hardness, the results may be confusing, and accurate sorting will not be possible.

Before serious consideration is given to the use of electromagnetic testing, it is strongly recommended that an equipment manufacturer be consulted about the possibilities for the specific application.

Fig. 15 High-speed eddy-current tester used for checking hardness of ball bearings

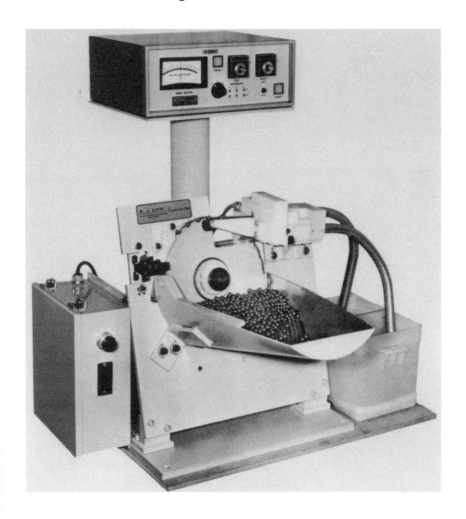

Balls are sorted for hardness within 1 to 2 points Rockwell C hardness accuracy at 25,000/h. Equipment accommodates a wide range of diameters. A proximity sensor detects all balls exiting the reject chute
Courtesy of K.J. Law Engineers, Inc.

Chapter 7

Hardness Testing Applications

Hardness Testing of Nonhomogeneous Materials

Accurate hardness values on nonhomogeneous materials often are difficult to attain, because of the presence of free graphite or pores. These constituents vary greatly in hardness between or among themselves, thus compounding the problem. Cast irons, P/M parts, and cemented carbides represent three such materials.

Cast Irons. Conventional hardness measurements of cast irons always indicate lower values than the true hardness of the metal matrix. This discrepancy, which is more pronounced in gray iron than in ductile and malleable irons, occurs because conventional hardness readings are composite values that reflect the hardnesses of both the matrix material and soft graphite. This is illustrated in Fig. 1. The black areas are graphitic carbon, which has essentially no hardness.

Provided that the test impression is made on a smooth, flat surface of adequate size, a Brinell hardness tester using a 10-mm ball (0.40-in.) penetrator and a 3000-kg load will determine the average hardness of malleable irons with reasonable accuracy. The hardness value, by virtue of the size of the ball penetrator, is representative of the gross structure under test.

Fig. 1 Class 30 gray iron as-cast in a sand mold

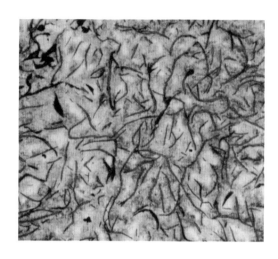

Type A graphite flakes in a matrix of 20% free ferrite (light constituent) and 80% pearlite (dark constituent). 3% nital. 100x
Source: Metals Handbook, Atlas of Microstructures of Industrial Alloys, Vol. 7, 8th ed., ASM, 1972, p. 83

In determining the hardness of small castings, it is often impossible to use a Brinell tester; therefore, a Rockwell tester must be used. Conversions have been developed to compensate for the discrepancies inherent in hardness measurements made on malleable irons with the smaller Rockwell penetrator. Figures 2(a) and (b) show conversions from Brinell (HB) to Rockwell B and G (HRB and HRG) scales for malleable and pearlitic malleable irons, respectively. Figure 2(b) also shows HRC equivalents for HB values for pearlitic malleable iron. These conversions generally are accepted by producers of malleable iron.

Matrix hardness is determined more accurately by the Brinell test than by Rockwell hardness tests for most types of cast irons, although both require correction to obtain true matrix hardness. The microhardness test is the most accurate method for determining matrix hardness.

Comparative hardness readings of ten quenched and tempered ductile irons are given in Table 1. Observed HRC readings ranged from 3.8 to 8.3 points lower than those converted from microhardness readings.

Fig. 2 Hardness conversions for malleable cast iron

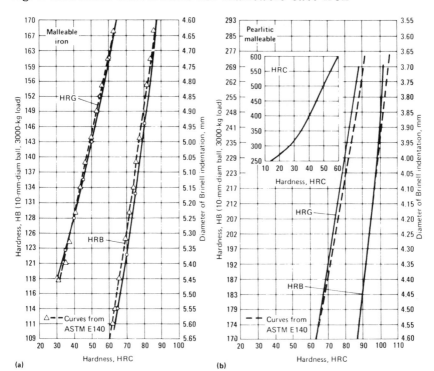

(a) Conversion from HB to HRB and HRG scales for malleable iron. (b) Conversion from HB to HRB, HRC and HRG scales for pearlitic malleable iron
Source: Metals Handbook, Heat Treating, Vol. 4, 9th ed., ASM, 1981, p. 526

Figure 3(a) shows the relationship between observed HRC readings and those converted from microhardness values for five gray irons of different carbon equivalents. Hardness measurements were taken at two laboratories after quenching and after tempering of each iron. The data in Fig. 3(a) show why the observed values obtained by conventional hardness testing may be misleading and help to explain the good wear resistance of gray irons with apparently low hardness.

Note that in Fig. 3(a) there is a correlation between carbon equivalent and hardness for all five irons tested. Carbon equivalent for a given gray or ductile iron is calculated as:

$$CE = \text{Total carbon} + (\% \text{ Si} + \% \text{ P})/3$$

Figure 3(a) also shows that, as carbon equivalent decreased, the discrepancy likewise decreased between HRC values converted from microhardness measurements (shown on the vertical scale) and observed hardness values measured by the HRC scale. As carbon equivalent decreases, the amount of free graphite also decreases. In addition, the discrepancy between the converted and observed hardness values diminishes at the lower hardness levels. Before a conversion chart can be used to obtain accurate results, it is necessary to know the carbon equivalent of the specific iron being tested.

Table 1   Comparative hardness values for quenched and tempered ductile irons

Iron	HB(a)	HRC converted from HB(b)	Observed HRC(c)	Microhard-ness, HV(d)	HRC converted from HV(b)	HRC converted from HV minus observed HRC
1	415	44.5	44.4	527	50.9	6.5
2	444	47.2	45.0	521	50.6	5.6
3	444	47.2	45.7	530	51.1	5.4
4	444	47.2	47.6	593	54.9	7.3
5	461	48.8	46.7	595	55.0	8.3
6	461	48.8	48.3	560	53.0	4.7
7	461	48.8	49.1	581	54.2	5.1
8	477	50.3	49.6	572	53.7	4.1
9	477	50.3	50.1	618	56.2	6.1
10	555	55.6	53.4	637	57.2	3.8

(a) Average of three readings for each iron. (b) Values based on SAE-ASM-ASTM hardness conversions for steel. (c) Average of five readings for each iron. (d) Average of a minimum of five readings for each iron; 100-kg load
Source: Metals Handbook, Heat Treating, Vol. 4, 9th ed., ASM, 1981, p. 526

Another comparison between observed and converted HRC values for gray and ductile irons is shown in Fig. 3(b). These irons were quenched in water from 900 °C (1650 °F) and tempered at 425 °C (800 °F) for 2 h.

P/M Parts. Because P/M parts may vary in density from less than 7 g/cm^3 to a density that approaches wrought materials, the discrepancy between apparent hardness and microhardness (true hardness values) can be very large and can vary widely. In addition, many P/M materials contain graphite carbon in various quantities, thus compounding the discrepancy caused by porosity (see Fig. 4).

Fig. 3 Relationship between observed and converted hardness values for gray and ductile irons

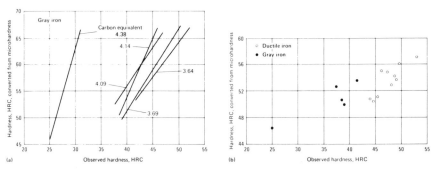

(a) | Observed hardness, HRC | (b) | Observed hardness, HRC

(a) Relationship, as influenced by carbon equivalent, for gray iron containing type 3 graphite. (b) Relationship for gray and ductile irons quenched in water from 900 °C (1650 °F) and tempered 2 h at 425 °C (800 °F)
Source: **Metals Handbook, Heat Treating**, *Vol. 4, 9th ed., ASM, 1981, p. 527*

Fig. 4 Microstructure of a sintered iron-graphite compact

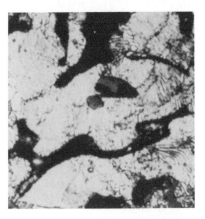

Iron powder mixed with graphite, pressed to a density of 6.1 g/cm³ and sintered at 1121 °C (2050 °F), which resulted in some spheroidization of the pores and further increases in bonding and transverse-rupture strength (to about 80 ksi, or 552 MPa). Combined carbon remained at 0.70%. Lighter constituent is pearlite; dark constituent is graphite and porosity. 4% picral plus 0.5% HNO₃. 800x
Source: **Metals Handbook, Atlas of Microstructures of Industrial Alloys**, *Vol. 7, 8th ed., ASM, 1972, p. 205*

Porous materials exhibit wider variation in hardness testing than their wrought counterparts. The entrance of the indenter into pores or groups of pores generally causes this effect. The seller and user of P/M materials should agree on which area or areas of a part are to be hardness tested. At least five consistent readings should be taken, in addition to any obviously high or low readings, which should be discarded. The remaining five readings should be averaged. Because most published data show typical hardness values, the buyer and seller must agree on specified or minimum values. The average of five or more consistent readings must meet the standard hardness, not any single reading.

Because of the variety of compositions and densities involved with P/M parts, recommendations for test methods is difficult. However, for the most part, the Rockwell test with a variety of scales is the most practical and most often used. A summary of the common P/M materials and the Rockwell scales used for testing is presented in Table 2. Frequently, trial and error testing is needed to establish the ideal test scale for a specific P/M material.

Table 2 Common hardness scales used for P/M parts

Material	Sintered hardness scale	Heat treated hardness scale
Iron	HRH, HRB	HRB, HRC
Iron-carbon	HRB	HRB, HRC
Iron-nickel-carbon	HRB	HRC
Prealloyed steel	HRB	HRC
Bronze	HRH	. . .
Brass	HRH	. . .

Source: Metals Handbook, Powder Metallurgy, Vol. 7, 9th ed., ASM, 1984, p. 489

Unlike fully dense materials, high hardness does not mean high tensile strength. Approximately 15 to 30% fine pearlite in iron-carbon sintered materials improves tensile strength; consequently, it is evident that high hardness values are not an indicator of high strength. Because P/M steels exhibit low hardenability, hardness specifications should be based on parts that have demonstrated successful service.

Although not widely used, the Rockwell B scale may be combined with a carbide ball for testing and controlling hardened parts. Scattering of data is minimized with the Rockwell B 1.58-mm (1/16-in.) diameter ball, and it is useful up to 120 HRB.

Microhardness of porous materials can best be measured with Knoop or diamond pyramid hardness indenters at loads of 100 g or greater. In atomized irons, particles exhibit minimal porosity; consequently, the Knoop indenter is suitable. It makes a very shallow indentation and is infrequently disturbed by entering undisclosed pores. Care should be taken in preparing the sample surface. On the other hand, the diamond pyramid indenter is particularly well suited to irons that contain numerous fine internal pores. Because of its greater depth of penetration, the diamond pyramid indenter frequently encounters hidden pores. Microhardness testing and the measurement of effective case depth are covered by Metal Powder Industries Federation standard MPIF 37.

For examining tempered steels, a light etching in 2% nital for 6 s is recommended. Fine pearlite appears as dark areas, unresolved at 1000x. Martensite appears light colored, with little or no evidence of platelets or needles (Fig. 5). This degree of etching enhances clarity and contrast for measuring the diamond indentation. Subsequent darker etching clearly shows the martensite needles and any retained austenite or carbides. Picral (4%) is recommended for subsequent etching (15 s) by immersion.

For microhardness testing of sintered steels, care must be taken in the definition of a case and the choice of microconstituent to be tested. For example, in a carburized and quenched nickel steel with 0.3% C in the core, martensite, fine pearlite, ferrite, and nickel-rich areas are visible. Nickel-rich areas should be ignored. The surface is nearly all martensite with some fine pearlite. If 50 HRC is defined as the case depth cut-off, the existence of a fine pearlite colony, that is below 50 HRC, would indicate that the reading was taken beneath the case. Case may be defined as the point where there is less than 50% martensite by area, or where the hardness falls below the 50 HRC equivalent. By comparison, in testing a wrought material without porosity, a heavier load that makes a large indentation should be used, thus averaging the microstructures while pinpointing the 50 HRC equivalent. In a P/M steel, this would result in the pores being averaged in with the other phase.

Fig. 5 Hardened and tempered Fe-0.8C alloy

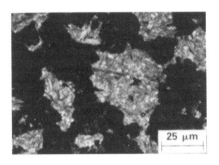

Light areas are martensite (60 HRC); dark areas are fine pearlite (40 HRC). 4% picral
Source: Metals Handbook, Powder Metallurgy, Vol. 7, 9th ed., ASM, 1984, p. 489

The use of light loads (under 100 g) causes errors when converting to the Rockwell C scale, if the 500-g Rockwell conversion table is used. An alternative is to provide individualized calibrations by removing pieces from several Rockwell standard blocks of hardnesses ranging from 20 to 60 HRC and metallographically mounting the working faces. These standards are carefully polished, allowing a direct calibration to be made between the Rockwell C scale and the length of the indentation. When this calibration is graphed, an unknown sample can be taken, the length (in filar units) of the hardness indentation made at 100 g can be measured, and the filar units can be converted to Rockwell C values.

Cemented carbides generally are comprised of two distinctly different materials; thus, by some definitions, they are considered composites. Because cemented carbides are produced by sintering, they may also contain tiny voids. However, the amount of void area usually is not enough to complicate hardness testing.

A typical cemented carbide is illustrated in Fig. 6. The light-colored matrix is cobalt and serves to bind the carbide particles together. The cobalt binder is relatively soft and is not worth considering in the total hardness. In this instance, as shown in Fig. 6, this soft ingredient occupies approximately 20% of the area, whereas the remaining 80% consists of hard carbide particles that have hardness values of 9 on Mohs scale (diamond is 10) or 1500 DPH and above. Obviously, no single test could register true hardness of this material. Only microhardness testing is capable of registering true hardness values. However, there are practical approaches that can be used to compare different cemented carbides, thus serving as a means of quality control.

Fig. 6 Particles of tungsten carbide (dark-gray constituent) in a matrix of cobalt (light-gray areas)

80% WC, 20% Co; density, 13.6 g/cm³. Murakami's reagent.
1500x
Source: **Metals Handbook, Atlas of Microstructures of Industrial Alloys**, *Vol. 7, 8th ed., ASM, 1972, p. 129*

Cemented carbides are tested on the A scale of the Rockwell tester which yields better diamond life than the C scale. To obtain accurate results, only diamond penetrators designated for A scale testing of cemented carbides should be used. Special cemented carbides for A scale test blocks should be used for checking the Rockwell tester, on which such tests are to be conducted.

Hardness Testing of Nonferrous Metals

With very few exceptions, nonferrous metals are substantially softer than steels and cast irons. Therefore, Brinell testing with a 500-g load (see Chapter 2), and Rockwell testing with steel ball penetrators with a variety of loads are the testing methods used most often, although diamond indenters are sometimes used, notably Rockwell A scale.

For the most part, hardness testing of nonferrous metals is simpler than for steels and cast irons. In the first place, most nonferrous metals are homogeneous to the extent that almost any indenter readings convey accurate information. Also, nonferrous metals do not involve hard surfaces, or surface decarburization, conditions that complicate hardness testing of ferrous metals.

To a great extent, the same general guidelines that pertain to other hardness testing methods apply to nonferrous as well as ferrous materials. This refers to indentation spacing, proximity to edges, thickness of the test material, and selection of the indenter and load combination that produces a reasonable and readable indentation.

Typical Rockwell scales used for a wide variety of nonferrous metals (some other materials are included) are presented in Table 3. Many of the higher strength or higher hardness nonferrous metals can be accurately tested by the Brinell tester, provided the workpiece is of sufficient thickness and size. The larger Brinell indentation will not impair the usefulness of the part. The 500-kg load is used most often for testing nonferrous metals. Very small nonferrous metal parts made of extremely thin sheet, strip, or foil are tested by the microhardness approach; either Vickers or Knoop indenters may be used.

Aluminum and aluminum alloys are tested frequently for hardness to distinguish between annealed, cold worked, and heat treated grades. The Rockwell B scale (100-kg load with a 1.58-mm, or 1/16-in., steel ball indenter) is generally well suited for testing grades that have been precipitation hardened to relatively high strength levels. For softer grades and down to nearly pure aluminum, hardness testing usually is done with the F, E, and H scales in that order, because the hardness and strength of the work metal decrease.

Table 3   Typical applications of regular Rockwell hardness scales

Scale(a)	Typical applications
B	Copper alloys, soft steels, aluminum alloys, malleable iron
C	Steel, hard cast irons, pearlitic malleable iron, titanium, deep case-hardened steel and other materials harder than HRB 100
A	Cemented carbides, thin steel and shallow case-hardened steel
D	Thin steel and medium case-hardened steel and pearlitic malleable iron
E	Cast iron, aluminum and magnesium alloys, bearing metals
F	Annealed copper alloys, thin soft sheet metals
G	Phosphor bronze, beryllium copper, malleable irons. Upper limit is HRG 92, to avoid possible flattening of ball.
H	Aluminum, zinc, lead
K, L, M, P, R, S, V	Bearing metals and other very soft or thin materials. Use smallest ball and heaviest load that do not give anvil effect.

(a) The N scales of a superficial hardness tester are used for materials similar to those tested on the Rockwell C, A, and D scales, but of thinner gage or case depth. The T scales are used for materials similar to those tested on the Rockwell B, F, and G scales, but of thinner gage. When minute indentations are required, a superficial hardness tester should be used. The W, X, and Y scales are used for very soft materials
Source: MEI Course 12, "Mechanical Testing of Metals," Lesson 3, "Hardness Testing," ASM, 1983, p. 17

To begin a testing program, the F scale with a 60-kg load and 1.58-mm (1/16-in.) steel ball is used first. Then the E scale with a 100-kg load and a 3.18-mm (1/8-in.) steel ball is tried. Finally, for the low alloys or nearly pure aluminum in the annealed condition, the H scale (60-kg load and a 3.18-mm or 1/8-in. steel ball) is used. For these scales, it is assumed that the gage is relatively heavy, thus not involving an anvil effect.

For hardness testing of thin gages of aluminum, the 15T and 30T scales of the Rockwell superficial tester are recommended. In general, the practices recommended for Rockwell testing in Chapter 3 are applicable to hardness testing of aluminum. When the test material is of adequate thickness and when the impressions are not objectionable, many of the aluminum alloys can be accurately tested with the Brinell test, using a 500-kg load (see Chapter 2).

Copper and Copper Alloys. Because the various copper alloys vary so widely in hardness, a wide range of indenters and loads is required to obtain accurate results. Beginning at the top of the range, the precipitation-hardenable alloys, such as C17000, C17200, and C17300, may be regarded as essentially the same as steel in their hardened condition, because they are generally within the hardness range of 36 to 45 HRC. Therefore, these alloys can be tested satisfactorily with the Rockwell C scale, or for thinner gages, the 15H or 30H scales are used. The Brinell test with 1500- to 3000-kg loads is also appropriate for testing harder copper alloys. For a large portion of the copper alloys in the annealed or cold worked condition, the Rockwell B scale is recommended, or the 15T or 30T scales for very thin sections.

When the indenter is penetrating the test material too deeply with the B scale, a lighter load with the E, F, or H scales must be used. Table 1 lists the Rockwell scales to be used for copper alloys.

In all cases, the thickness of the work metal should be at least ten times the depth of the indentation for Rockwell or Brinell testing. For extremely thin sheet or foil, or for small delicate workpieces, the microhardness testers must be used for accurate hardness evaluation.

Magnesium and magnesium alloys are tested by using the Rockwell B scale, although for the softer, annealed alloys, the indenter size is increased to 1/8 using the E scale. As for other metals and alloys, thin sections of magnesium alloys must be tested with 15T or 30T scales to avoid anvil effect.

Titanium. The A scale of the Rockwell hardness tester is best suited for testing titanium. The use of the 60-kg load tends to increase the life of the diamond penetrator, because there is an affinity between diamond and titanium, which usually shortens diamond life. Titanium tends to adhere to the tip of the diamond penetrator and can readily be removed with 3/0 paper when the penetrator is rotated in a lathe. Maintaining a clean diamond will give more reliable results.

Zinc in sheet form may be tested for hardness, but the length of time for applying the major load of the Rockwell test must be carefully controlled to 15 s, because this material will flow under the applied test load. The E scale is used for sheet down to 3.18 mm (0.125 in.) and the H scale for sheet to 1.27 mm (0.050 in.) gage. For thinner sheet, the 15T or 30T scale of the Rockwell superficial tester should be used.

Hardness Testing of Nonmetallic Materials

Plastic materials commonly are evaluated for hardness by using either a Rockwell tester with a variety of indenter and load combinations, a microhardness tester, or a Durometer. Rubbers and rubber-like materials are usually tested with a Durometer.

Hardness Testing of Plastics

Hardness testing of plastics presents many variables that do not relate to the testing of metals. Because plastics are time-sensitive and continue to flow under load when tested for hardness, the time factor must be considered at three different stages of the test. Therefore, plastics are tested according to ASTM D785. The procedure is:

- Set the dial gage within 10 s. If the major load is applied immediately after the dial gage is set, it is not necessary to apply a time factor after the minor load is applied. However, it is desirable to specify some time interval--10 s, for example--as the period within which the minor load is applied, the dial gage is set, and the major load is applied.

- Apply the major load for 15 s. The application time of the major load must be controlled carefully, if reproducible results are to be obtained. Fifteen seconds after the major load has been released has been found to be satisfactory.

- Read the Rockwell hardness number 15 s after removal of the major load.

The penetrators generally used for testing plastics are 3.18. 6.35, and 12.7 mm (0.125, 0.25, and 0.50 in.) diameter balls, at major loads of 60, 100, and 150 kg. Because of the creep and recovery characteristics of plastics, the time factors referred to above should be carefully controlled.

Hardness tests are really an indication of cure of some thermosetting materials and an indication of punching quality of laminated sheet stock. For best results, specimens should be conditioned for temperature and humidity before testing.

There is some agreement between some hardness orders and the order of the Alpha scale of the Rockwell tester. However, the M scale of the Rockwell tester shows a difference in order of hardness, which is probably due to recovery of the specimen on removal of the major load. The long diagonal of the Knoop indentation is affected minimally by elastic recovery.

By including values for the M, L, and R scales of the Rockwell tester, an idea of the sensitivity and overlapping of the scales may be obtained. The amount of recovery will vary with scale, elasticity of material, and with the weight of the major load.

For metals, excluding shapes such as tubes, the movement of the dial gage that is caused by the elasticity of the metal being tested is small and not considered to be a disadvantage when making the test. Elasticity may reach considerable proportions with plastics. In addition to the spring of the frame of the tester, elasticity may prevent full application of the major load because of limitations in the design of the tester.

The limitation of the standard model Rockwell tester is considered to be 150 dial gage divisions under a 150-kg load. This figure represents the number of divisions of travel on the dial gage due to penetration into the material under test, spring of the frame, penetrator, plunger rod system, and elasticity of the material under test, while the major load is applied. Special Rockwell testers, designated as PL models, increase this limitation to 250 divisions under a load of 150 kg.

To determine whether the machine limitation is being exceeded and whether the major load is being fully applied, the major load is applied in the following manner. With the major load still applied, an additional load is applied by manually exerting pressure on the weights on the machine; the dial gage needle then should indicate additional penetration. If not, the full major load may not be acting (due to reaching limit of depth of indentation), and faulty readings may result. In this case, the manufacturer should be contacted.

Use of the Alpha Scale. A variation of the standard Rockwell test is often used for testing plastics. This is referred to as the Alpha Rockwell hardness number in Procedure B of ASTM D785.

The standard Rockwell tester is used with a major load of 60 kg and 12.7-mm (0.50-in.) ball penetrator. The test is made by applying the minor load in the usual manner, setting the dial to set, and applying the 60-kg major load for 15 s. With the major load applied, the number of divisions the penetrator has traveled from set is read on the dial gage. From this figure, the spring of the tester is subtracted, determined under a major load of 60 kg, and then the remainder is subtracted from 150.

The spring of the machine, known as the "spring constant," is determined as follows: (1) Place a soft copper block of sufficient thickness and with plane parallel surfaces on the anvil in the normal testing position; (2) raise the sample and the anvil by the capstan screw, until the large pointer is at the set position; and (3) apply the major load by tripping the load release lever. The dial gage then will indicate the vertical distance of indentation, plus the spring of the machine frame and any other elastic compressible deformation of the plunger rod system and penetrator. Repeat this operation several times without moving the block. However, the dial must be reset after each test while under minor load, until the deflection of the dial gage becomes constant, that is, until no further indentation takes place, and only the spring of the instrument remains. This value, in terms of dial divisions, is the spring constant.

The advantage of the alpha scale is that it provides a scale covering the range of plastics. Those interested in plastics testing should refer to ASTM D785.

Table 4 Specifications of Durometers

Durometer type	Main spring	Indenter	For use on:
A (conforms to ASTM D 2240) ...... 822 g		Frustum cone	Soft vulcanized rubber and all elastomeric materials, natural rubber, GR-S, GR-1, neoprene, nitrile rubbers, Thiokol, flexible polyester cast resins, polyacrylic esters, wax, felt, leather, etc.
B .... 822 g		Sharp 30° included angle	Moderately hard rubber such as typewriter rollers, platens, etc.
C .... 20 lb		Frustum cone	Medium hard rubber and plastics
D (conforms to ASTM D 2240) ...... 10 lb		Sharp 30° included angle	Hard rubber and the harder grades of plastics such as rigid thermoplastic sheet. Plexiglas, polystyrene, vinyl sheet, cellulose acetate and thermosetting laminates such as formica, paper-filled calendar rolls, calendar bowls, etc.
D0 .... 10 lb		3/32-in. sphere	Very dense textile windings, slasher beams, etc.
0 .... 822 g		3/32-in. sphere	Soft printers rollers, Artgum, medium-density textile windings of rayon, orlon, nylon, etc.
00 .... 4 oz		3/32-in. sphere	Sponge rubber and plastics, low-density textile windings; not for use on foamed latex
000 (available with round dial only) ..... 4 oz		1/2-in. diam. spherical	Ultrasoft sponge rubber and plastic
T .... 822 g		3/32-in. sphere	Medium-density textile windings on spools and bobbins with a maximum diamter of 100 mm (4 in.), types T and T-2 have a concave bottom plate to facilitate centering on cylindrical specimens

*Source: **Metals Handbook, Mechanical Testing**, Vol. 8, 9th ed., ASM, 1985, p. 107*

Durometer Testing

The Durometer is a well-known and widely used instrument for measuring hardness of virtually all types of plastics, rubbers, and various rubber-like materials. The Durometer measures hardness by means of indentation much like hardness testing of metals. However, the indenters used in Durometers are spring loaded instead of being forced by weights. Not unlike metals, nonmetallic materials vary greatly in hardness, thus requiring a variety of test instruments. Several types of Durometers have been developed that accommodate the full range of hardness, and specially developed instruments are available for testing O-rings and extremely thin materials. The various types available are listed in the left column of Table 4. However, only two (A and D) are covered in ASTM D2240.

Fig. 7 Round- and quadrant-style durometers

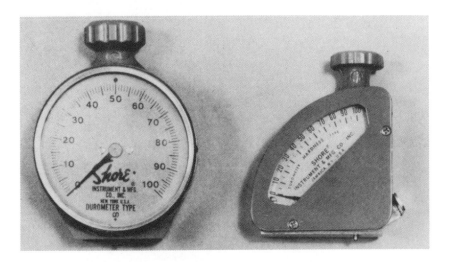

*Source: **Metals Handbook, Mechanical Testing**, Vol. 8, 9th ed., ASM, 1985, p. 107*

Types of Durometers. Most Durometers are available in either the quadrant or the round styles (see Table 4, and Fig. 7 and 8). Originally, Durometers were of the quadrant style (upper photo of Fig. 7). Round-style instruments (lower photo of Fig. 7) were introduced in 1944. They read the same as the quadrant-style in the same calibration category and satisfy the need for an instrument graduated in units rather than in increments of five. The sweep of the dial hand from 0 to 100 is 265° rather than 74°, as on quadrant-style instruments. Both the round and quadrant styles are used in the same manner.

Fig. 8 Durometers mounted in operating stands

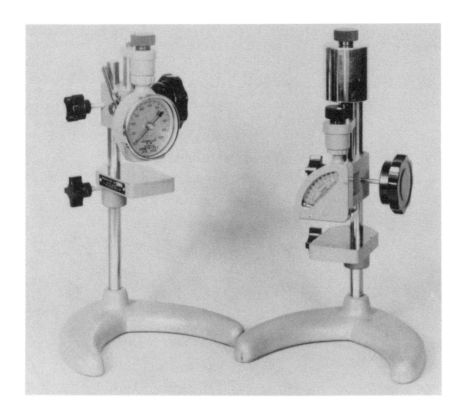

*Source: **Metals Handbook, Mechanical Testing**, Vol. 8, 9th ed., ASM, 1985, p. 108*

The pencil-type model (Fig. 9) is a relatively new Durometer. Not only is the pencil-type model even more portable than the other types (it is less than 127 mm (5 in.) high), but it is better adapted to taking readings on cylindrical items, such as rubber rollers.

Fig. 9 Pencil-type Durometer

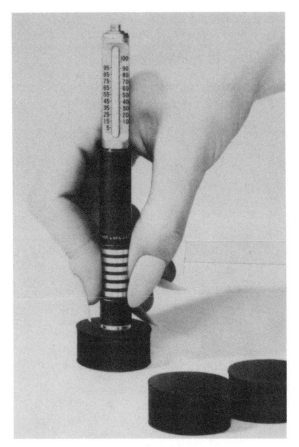

Courtesy of Shore Instrument and Manufacturing Co.

Durometers also are available with digital readout (Fig. 10). This instrument is capable of producing accurate and reproducible readings on the A scale for materials that are too thin for measurement by conventional instruments. This model (Fig. 10) comes in both analog and digital output to interface with a computer.

Applications. Durometers are used for measuring hardness of plastics and rubbers ranging from ultrasoft sponge rubbers to hard plastics. A list of test materials correlated with the specific type of Durometer, main spring data, and type of indenter is presented in Table 4. In some instances, Durometer test results can be converted to another scale. A partial conversion chart is shown in Fig. 11.

Fig. 10 Durometer with digital readout

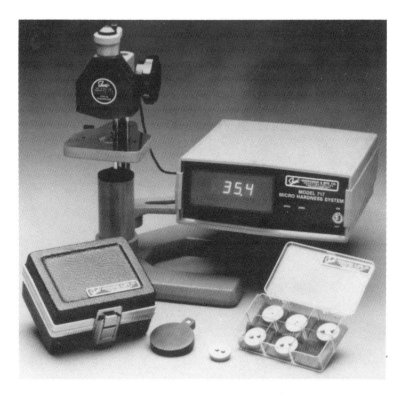

Courtesy of Shore Instrument and Manufacturing Co.

Special Applications for Hardness Testing

Determination of case depth on case hardened steels and evaluating hardenability of ferrous metals are two of the most notable applications for hardness testing.

Measurement of Case Depth. The role of the hardness test in case hardened steels is very important because it provides information about the hardness and depth of the case, i.e., the harder outside layer. The remaining material is known as the core.

Fig. 11 Durometer-Plastometer conversion chart

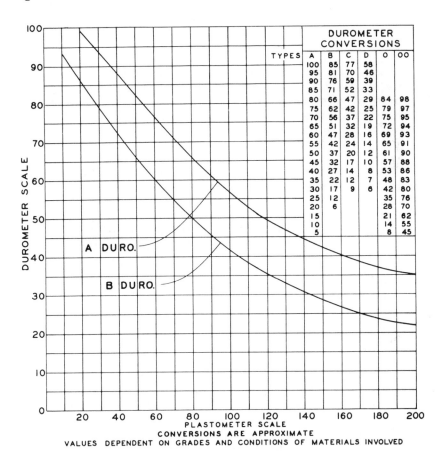

CONVERSIONS ARE APPROXIMATE
VALUES DEPENDENT ON GRADES AND CONDITIONS OF MATERIALS INVOLVED

Courtesy of Shore Instrument and Manufacturing Co.

Methods of measuring and interpreting results has often been controversial between heat treaters and users of the products. In addition to the hardness of the case, as determined by a test on the surface, knowledge of the depth of case often is valuable. The depth can be reported either as "effective case depth" or "total case depth."

Effective case depth is the distance normal to the surface of the hardened case to the point at which a specified level of hardness is maintained. This hardness is usually 50 HRC, unless otherwise specified.

Total case depth is the perpendicular distance from the surface to the point at which no difference in chemical or physical properties can be distinguished between the case and the core.

The most accurate and repeatable method of determining effective or total case depth is by means of some type of hardness traverse. A hardness traverse indicates the precise hardness characteristics from the edge to the core and should remove any controversy between the heat treater and the customer. It is of the utmost importance that the heat treater and the customer agree, in advance, on case depth and on how it is to be measured. This approach often will prevent rejection or rework of expensive workpieces.

The preferred means of evaluating case hardness and depth is by traverses made on polished cross sections (actual part or a representative coupon) measured by a microhardness tester. However, many shops do not have a microhardness tester, and there sometimes may be other reasons for using a less sophisticated method. One approach is described below.

In testing hardened material, it is essential that the depth of case is sufficient to support the penetration properly; this means the case depth should be at least ten times the depth of the indentation. As an example, the depth of the indentation of a 673 HRC test is approximately 0.0076 mm (0.003 in.); therefore, the case depth must be at least 0.076 mm (0.030 in.) if an accurate Rockwell C scale reading is to be obtained. This feature can be an advantage in controlling the depth of case. In this example, both Rockwell A and C scale tests are made. A Rockwell C scale reading less than 63 HRC indicates either a soft case or a case less than 0.076 mm (0.030 in.). If an A scale test is also made and a reading of 83 HRA is obtained, the case is hard, but less than 0.076 mm (0.030 in.). On the other hand, if the A scale value is less than 83 HRA, the case is too soft.

It also is possible to use either the Rockwell C or Rockwell A scales for making a form of hardness traverse on a cross section, as shown in Fig. 12(a) and (b). In Fig. 12(a), a tapered traverse is taken, which is better suited for light to medium depth of case depths than traverses more often used for deep cases as shown in Fig. 12(b).

Another approach for determining case hardness at different levels is illustrated in Fig. 12(c) and (d). In this instance, the indenter is perpendicular to the surface with no cross sectioning. Taper grinding often is done, as illustrated in Fig. 12(c), and is best suited for testing of light cases, whereas the step grinding technique generally is preferred for testing of deep cases.

Fig. 12 Methods of measuring case depth

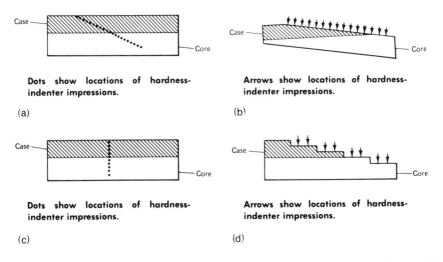

(a) Cross-sectioned specimen for hardness-traverse method of measuring depth of light and medium cases. (b) Cross-sectioned specimen for hardness-traverse method of measuring depth of medium and heavy cases. (c) Taper-ground specimen for hardness-traverse method of measuring depth of light and medium cases. (d) Step-ground specimen for hardness-traverse method of measuring depth of medium and heavy cases
Source: ***Metals Handbook, Heat Treating**, Vol. 4, 9th ed., ASM, 1981, p. 278*

For accurate results, tests must be spaced no closer than three diameters from center to center of the indentation. For this reason and because of the size of Rockwell indentations, hardness traverses should be made using the Knoop or DPH scales of the microhardness tester.

The superficial Rockwell scales with the 15-, 30- or 45-kg loads also may be used and may be advantageous, in some instances, because indentations can be spaced closer to each other.

Again, an agreement must be reached between heat treaters and customers. Probably the most popular approach is negotiated in terms of measuring the effective case depth, using the step grinding technique, as shown in Fig. 12(d). The step at which the hardness drops below 50 HRC is considered the end of the case. This test can be made quickly in the shop and allows little room for controversy.

Testing to Evaluate Hardenability. A number of hardenability tests have been devised, each having advantages and limitations. Most of these tests are either no longer used, or their use is restricted to specialized applications. All of these methods of testing for hardenability involve hardness testing--principally by means of the Rockwell C scale.

The end-quench test has proved to be the method with the highest degree of reproducibility and has thus been almost universally adopted for evaluating hardenability of virtually all standard alloy steels and for some grades of carbon steels. The test is relatively simple to perform and can produce much useful information for the designer, as well as for the fabricator.

Test Bars for the End-Quench Test. Although variations are sometimes made to accommodate specific requirements, the test bars for the end-quench test are normally 25 mm (1 in.) in diameter by 100 mm (4 in.) long. A 25.5-mm (1.004-in.) diameter collar is left on one end to hold it in a quenching jig (Fig. 13).

In this test, the water flow is controlled by a suitable valve, so that the amount striking the end of the specimen (Fig. 13) is constant in volume and velocity. The water impinges on the end of the specimen only; then it drains away. By this means, cooling rates vary from about the fastest possible on the quenched end to very slow, essentially equal to cooling in still air, on the opposite end. This results in a wide range of hardnesses along the length of the bar.

After the test bar has been quenched, two opposite and flat parallel surfaces are ground along the length of the bar to a depth of 0.381 mm (0.015 in.). Rockwell C hardness determinations then are made every 1.59 mm (0.0625 in.). A specimen-holding indexing fixture is helpful for this operation for convenience, as well as for accuracy. Such fixtures are available as accessory attachments for conventional Rockwell testers.

Fig. 13 Standard end-quench (Jominy) test specimen and method of quenching in quenching jig

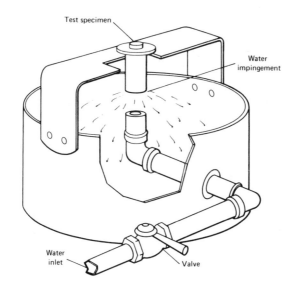

Source: **Heat Treater's Guide**, *ASM, 1982, p. 21*

The next step is to record the readings and plot them on graph paper to develop a curve, as illustrated in Fig. 14. By comparing the curves resulting from end-quench tests of different grades of steel, their relative hardenability may be established. The steels with higher hardenability will be harder at a given distance from the quenched end of the specimen than steels with lower hardenability. Thus, the flatter the curve, the greater the hardenability. On the end-quench curves, hardness usually is not measured beyond approximately 50 mm (2 in.), because hardness measurements beyond this distance are seldom of any significance. At about this 50-mm (2-in.) distance from the quenched end, the effect of water on the quenched end has deteriorated, and the effect of cooling from the surrounding air has become significant.

An absolutely flat curve demonstrates conditions of very high hardenability, which characterize an air-hardening steel such as some highly alloyed steels.

Fig. 14 Method of developing end-quench curve by plotting hardness versus distance from quenched end

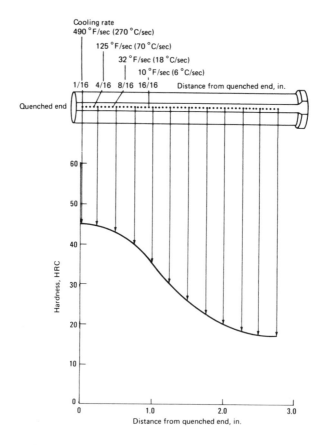

Cooling rate
490 °F/sec (270 °C/sec)
125 °F/sec (70 °C/sec)
32 °F/sec (18 °C/sec)
10 °F/sec (6 °C/sec)

1/16 4/16 8/16 16/16   Distance from quenched end, in.

Quenched end

Hardness, HRC

Distance from quenched end, in.

Hardness plotted every 1/4 in., although Rockwell C reading were taken in increments of 1/16 in., as shown at top of illustration
*Source: **Heat Treater's Guide**, ASM, 1982, p. 21*

Chapter 8

Selection of Hardness Testing Method

Selection of a hardness test method would be relatively simple, if the material being tested had the following characteristics: (1) was in the form of simple flat pieces with a minimum thickness of 3.18 mm (0.125 in.); (2) was comprised of homogeneous material; and (3) had a surface composition that was essentially the same as its center; that is, no hard case.

Furthermore, tests would be conducted under ideal testing conditions, so that interpreting the results would be relatively simple and could thus be accomplished by operators with minimal skills.

However, this is not the case, and there are a number of variables that may have a profound effect on the method selected, when the entire broad field of hardness testing is considered.

Selection Factors

The following represent most of the factors that require careful consideration in proper selection of a hardness testing program. The order of the listing does not necessarily represent their degree of importance.

- Hardness range of the test material

- Size of the workpiece

- Shape of the workpiece

- Degree of flatness of the workpiece

- Surface condition of the workpiece

- Nature of the test material--homogeneous, or nonhomogeneous

- Effect of indentation marks

- Equipment availability

- Number of identical pieces to be tested

Hardness Range of the Test Material. To select the optimum method of hardness testing, it is essential to have some knowledge of the hardness range, which can be determined from the general composition of the material and its processing history. In many instances, some trial and error is essential to arrive at the optimum method and technique.

For nonferrous metals, selection of a method is seldom a problem. The Rockwell B scale is probably used more than any other test and will usually suffice for testing most copper, aluminum, and magnesium alloys. At least the Rockwell B scale represents a good starting point. Should readings exceed 100 HRB, another scale should be selected--probably the Rockwell C scale. As a rule, Rockwell B readings in excess of 100 would occur only on heat treated copper alloys. On the other hand, if Rockwell B readings are below 50, the indenter is sinking too deep for accurate readings, and the load should be decreased, or the size of the indenter should be increased, as in the Rockwell E or F scales. Nonferrous metals also may be tested with the Brinell tester--usually with a 500-kg load. However, the accuracy of the Brinell test decreases rapidly when the size of the impression is less than 3 mm (0.12 in.) or more than 6 mm (0.24 in.). The approaches described above assume that the size and thickness of the work metal are compatible with the indentation depth.

Annealed, hot rolled, cold finished, forged, or cast carbon and alloy steels usually are tested by the Brinell or Rockwell

B tester. For sheet metal products the thickness also must be considered. Use of the Brinell test usually is precluded for sheet steel, and Rockwell B test also may be unsuitable, depending on thickness of the sheet. Thin sheet is usually tested by use of the 15 T or 30 T scales; see Chapter 3 for guidelines regarding the relationship of Rockwell scale and metal thickness.

Fully hardened, hardened, and tempered carbon, alloy, tool, and stainless steels are tested frequently by a diamond indenter, one of the Rockwell scales, Vickers, Scleroscope, or by one of the microhardness techniques. The Rockwell C test generally is used when conditions permit. Rockwell C readings of less than 20 (or its equivalent in other scales) should not be considered valid, and some inaccuracy can be expected, as the value drops below 30 HRC.

Cast or annealed gray, ductile, compacted graphite, and malleable irons are tested most frequently by the Brinell tester. The Rockwell B tester is used also, notably for small castings. However, the graphite phase of these irons always results in observed readings that are less than actual; the degree is based largely on the carbon equivalent of the iron. Quenched and tempered irons commonly are tested by the Rockwell C scale, but again the discrepancy between observed and actual may be large. White irons and other special varieties usually are tested by the Rockwell C test. True hardness evaluations of any cast iron are obtained only by microhardness testing.

Size of the workpiece may not only affect technique, but can have a profound effect on selection of method. When the weight of a workpiece exceeds 16 to 23 kg (35 to 50 lb), it is rarely practical to make hardness tests with the conventional Brinell or Rockwell testers described in Chapters 2 and 3. Therefore, for larger workpieces that are not easily transported to the stationary testers, the logical procedure is to take the testers to the workpiece. Portable machines often are used for on-site testing of workpieces that are too large and/or unwieldy to transport to the tester.

For many applications where on-site testing is required, the Scleroscope can be a great advantage (see Chapter 6). Likewise, ultrasonic instruments can be used for on-site testing. However, when using either Scleroscope or ultrasonic testing, surface condition is critical to obtaining accurate results. Neither is well suited for testing cast irons.

Numbers of similar parts to be tested that are large and heavy may also influence the methods and techniques selected for hardness testing. Regular testing of similar workpieces may warrant special setups.

Shape of the Workpiece. Obviously, the ideal shape for hardness testing would be a square block of sufficient size to permit making any kind of indentations as may be needed. However, such ideal conditions seldom exist, so that arrangements must be made to accommodate a variety of shapes. Probably, the first step in dealing with different shapes is to have available a variety of anvils for either Rockwell or Brinell testing.

There are several possibilities for dealing with unwieldy parts (long shafts and others). Outboard supports or counterweights are two possibilities. Another approach is to use a type of tester that firmly clamps the workpiece, before the load is applied.

Round ring-like parts often are tested by using special adapters or specially designed instruments. Cylindrical parts can be tested accurately by either the Brinell or Rockwell methods with the use of correction factors. In Brinell testing of cylindrical surfaces, an oval indentation results, but this can be corrected to a reasonable degree by taking the average of two optical readings taken at right angles to each other.

Degree of Flatness. An absolutely flat surface is ideal for making any hardness test, but some methods are more sensitive to this condition than are others; mainly because, for some methods, there are means of compensating for out-of-flatness.

For accurate readings from Brinell, Rockwell, Scleroscope, and conventional microhardness testers, the surface being tested should be at least within 2 or 3° of flatness; that is, close to 90° of the direction of travel of the indenter. For example, for odd-shaped workpieces that do not have any surfaces that are parallel to the surface to be tested, it is often possible to provide adjustable fixtures, which can be tilted as required to allow a flat surface for testing. This is very often done with either the Brinell or the Rockwell tester.

For microhardness testing, securing and holding devices are used to attain a test surface that is sufficiently flat. Similar approaches have been used for Brinell and Rockwell testing;

frequently, they are specially designed for specific workpieces. Ultrasonic microhardness tests may be performed on surfaces that are not flat, because different principles are involved.

Surface conditions is a term intended to cover two different conditions, both of which pertain to selection of the optimum method and/or testing technique. First, surface finish must be considered. In general, the degree of surface smoothness that is required for accurate results is related directly to the size of the indenter. Although the smoother finishes are highly desirable for any testing method, the Brinell test, which involves a large indenter, can be made and read with a reasonable degree of accuracy when the finish is comparable to finish machined or rough ground.

For Rockwell testing, a finish ground surface is generally about the minimum for obtaining accurate readings, whereas polished surfaces are preferred. For Vickers testing and on through microhardness testing (including Scleroscope testing), the finish requirements are far more stringent. At the opposite extreme from the Brinell test is microhardness testing with very light loads (less than 100 g). At this extreme, the workpiece or specimen requires a surface finish equal to that used for microscopic examination at high magnification. It is, therefore, obvious that the degree of smoothness that can be attained can have a profound effect on which hardness test method is selected.

The other surface condition that may affect the selection of the hardness test method is surface composition (generally unique to steels). Decarburization, retained austenite, carburization, or other composition changes that result in a hard case are likely to influence the choice of the hardness test method, or methods. In many instances, differences in surface conditions require use of more than one method or scale.

Nature of the Test Material. How the specific metal or metal alloy has been prepared may have a profound effect on the method and technique selected for hardness testing; that is, whether the test part or specimen was taken from a rolled bar, forged, cast, or prepared from metal powders (P/M parts).

Although there have been exceptions, as a rule, parts made from rolled products or forgings of the same composition can be considered the same as far as hardness testing is concerned.

Similarly, cast versions of steels and nonferrous metals usually may be given the same consideration as their forged or rolled counterparts. Only in rare cases is the density low enough in the cast version to affect the hardness test method or to require a correction factor.

As described in Chapter 7, cast irons represent an entirely different testing situation because of the graphite phase, which has no measurable hardness. Because the amount of graphite varies, the correction factor also varies with the carbon equivalent. In general, the degree of error caused by the graphite decreases as the size of the indenter increases. Therefore, the Brinell test is the preferred method of hardness testing cast iron. For extremely hard grades (heat treated or chilled), it may be necessary to use diamond indenters (the Rockwell C test is most commonly used). Under these conditions, the true hardness, in terms of wear resistance, can be determined accurately only by knowing the carbon equivalent of the iron. For a complete understanding of the hardness value of a given iron, microhardness testing is the best approach.

Many P/M parts contain graphite, and in addition, voids introduce a new problem in making accurate hardness evaluations. Rockwell testing using a variety of steel ball indenters and loads is the most common procedure for P/M parts (see Chapter 7). As for cast iron, the true hardness characteristics of P/M parts can be determined only by individual measurement of the constituents.

Effect of Indentation Marks. Marks left by indentation hardness testing can range from more than 4 mm (0.16 in.) in diameter, as in the Brinell test, down to a microscopic mark left from light-load microhardness testing. Consequently, the presence (or absence) of test marks could be important in selecting a test procedure.

In most instances, the presence of Brinell impressions on workpieces such as forgings and castings is not objectionable. On a finished part, however, a mark as large as a Brinell impression may be objectionable from the appearance standpoint, or in some cases can interfere with its function. There are notable cases where analysis of a service failure proved that a fracture was nucleated by a Brinell impression. In other cases, damage was found to be inflicted immediately. For example, a lot of small malleable iron castings required 100% inspection for hardness by the Brinell test. For this particular application, Brinell testing was a poor selection. Subsequently, magnetic particle testing revealed small cracks emanating from the indentation marks, so that practically all of the castings were scrapped.

Rockwell indentation marks also can have a deleterious effect, although because the indentations are much smaller, the likelihood of damage is generally less compared with Brinell marks. Generally, diamond indenter marks are not sufficient to impair the function of a part, except in the case of precision parts used for purposes such as in fuel control systems. Rarely are marks that are left by the Scleroscope or microhardness testers objectionable.

Effect of Production Quantities and Production Flow. The number of identical or similar parts to be tested may make a difference in selecting the method as well as the technique for hardness testing. Also, whether the parts are simply a batch, or whether production flow is fairly constant, may influence the selection of the test procedure. The Scleroscope does lend itself to very rapid testing, when specific conditions exist; therefore, it is used frequently for high-production testing. Likewise, under certain conditions, the ultrasonic hardness test can be used for microhardness testing of many identical parts.

As a rule, however, mass-production hardness testing is done with either the Brinell or the Rockwell testers. Either of these instruments is available in partly or completely automated setups; even to the degree that rejects are automatically separated. For extremely high-production testing, hardness evaluation by sorting is the most logical approach.

A hardness testing problem involving mass production should be discussed with one or more than one manufacturer of hardness testing equipment. A listing of manufacturers is included in the Appendices.

Appendix 1 Hardness Conversion Tables

From a practical standpoint, it is important to be able to convert the results of one type of hardness test into those of a different test. Because a hardness test does not measure a well-defined property of a material and because all tests in common use are not based on the same types of measurements, it is not surprising that universal hardness-conversion relationships have not been developed.

Hardness conversions are empirical relationships. The most reliable hardness-conversion data exist for steel, which is harder than 240 HB. The following tables for conversion among Rockwell, Brinell, and Diamond Pyramid hardness are applicable to heat treated carbon and alloy steels and to almost all alloy constructional steels and tool steels in the as-forged, annealed, normalized, and quenched and tempered conditions. However, different conversion tables are required for materials with greatly different elastic moduli, or with greater strain-hardening capacity. Conversion tables for nickel and high-nickel alloys, cartridge brass, austenitic stainless steel sheet and plate, and copper can be found in ASTM E140, "Standard Hardness Conversion Tables for Metals."

The indentation hardness of soft metals depends on the strain-hardening behavior of the material during the test, which in turn is dependent on the previous degree of strain hardening of the material before the test. The modulus of elasticity also has been shown to influence conversions at high hardness levels. At low hardness levels, conversions between hardness scales measuring depth and those measuring diameter are likewise influenced by differences in the modulus of elasticity. The standard procedure for reporting converted hardness numbers indicates the measured hardness and test scale in parentheses--for example, 451 HB (48 HRC).

Fig. 1 Hardness conversion for steel

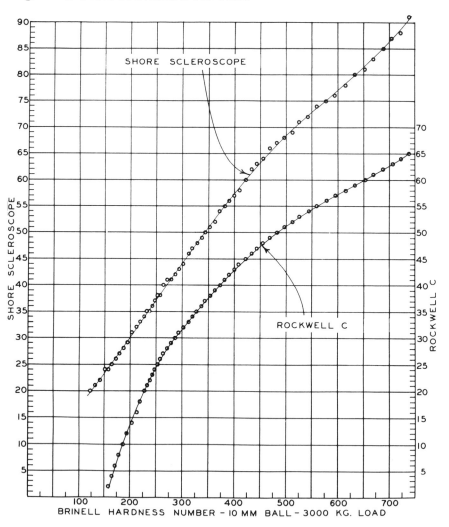

Conversions are approximate and subject to variations depending on the material being tested, its analysis, surface finish, shape, mass and homogeneity. Data are based on ASTM E48-43T and **Machinery's Handbook**

Approximate equivalent hardness numbers for Rockwell B hardness numbers for steel(a)

Rockwell hardness No.	Vickers hardness No.	Brinell hardness No., 10-mm ball 500-kg load	Brinell hardness No., 10-mm ball 3000-kg load	Rockwell hardness No. A scale, 60-kg load, diamond indenter	Rockwell hardness No. C scale, 150-kg load, indenter	Rockwell hardness No. F scale, 60-kg load, 1/16-in.- diam ball	Rockwell superficial 15T scale, 15-kg load	Rockwell superficial 30T scale, 30-kg load	Rockwell superficial 45T scale, 45-kg load	Knoop hardness No., 500-g load and greater	Scleroscope hardness No.
98	228	189	228	60.2	(19.9)	...	92.5	81.8	70.9	241	34
97	222	184	222	59.5	(18.6)	...	92.1	81.1	69.9	236	33
96	216	179	216	58.9	(17.2)	...	91.8	80.4	68.9	231	32
95	210	175	210	58.3	(15.7)	...	91.5	79.8	67.9	226	...
94	205	171	205	57.6	(14.3)	...	91.2	79.1	66.9	221	31
93	200	167	200	57.0	(13.0)	...	90.8	78.4	65.9	216	30
92	195	163	195	56.4	(11.7)	...	90.5	77.8	64.8	211	...
91	190	160	190	55.8	(10.4)	...	90.2	77.1	63.8	206	29
90	185	157	185	55.2	(9.2)	...	89.9	76.4	62.8	201	28
89	180	154	180	54.6	(8.0)	...	89.5	75.8	61.8	196	27
88	176	151	176	54.0	(6.9)	...	89.2	75.1	60.8	192	...
87	172	148	172	53.4	(5.8)	...	88.9	74.4	59.8	188	26
86	169	145	169	52.8	(4.7)	...	88.6	73.8	58.8	184	26
85	165	142	165	52.3	(3.6)	...	88.2	73.1	57.8	180	25
84	162	140	162	51.7	(2.5)	...	87.9	72.4	56.8	176	...
83	159	137	159	51.1	(1.4)	...	87.6	71.8	55.8	173	24
82	156	135	156	50.6	(0.3)	...	87.3	71.1	54.8	170	24
81	153	133	153	50.0	...	...	86.9	70.4	53.8	167	...
80	150	130	150	49.5	...	...	86.6	69.7	52.8	164	23
79	147	128	147	48.9	...	...	86.3	69.1	51.8	161	...
78	144	126	144	48.4	...	...	86.0	68.4	50.8	158	22
77	141	124	141	47.9	...	...	85.6	67.7	49.8	155	22
76	139	122	139	47.3	...	...	85.3	67.1	48.8	152	...
75	137	120	137	46.8	...	99.6	85.0	66.4	47.8	150	21
74	135	118	135	46.3	...	99.1	84.7	65.7	46.8	148	21
73	132	116	132	45.8	...	98.5	84.3	65.1	45.8	145	...
72	130	114	130	45.3	...	98.0	84.0	64.4	44.8	143	20
71	127	112	127	44.8	...	97.4	83.7	63.7	43.8	141	20
70	125	110	125	44.3	...	96.8	83.4	63.1	42.8	139	...
69	123	109	123	43.8	...	96.2	83.0	62.4	41.8	137	19
68	121	107	121	43.3	...	95.6	82.7	61.7	40.8	135	19
67	119	106	119	42.8	...	95.1	82.4	61.0	39.8	133	19
66	117	104	117	42.3	...	94.5	82.1	60.4	38.7	131	...
65	116	102	116	41.8	...	93.9	81.8	59.7	37.7	129	18
64	114	101	114	41.4	...	93.4	81.4	59.0	36.7	127	18
63	112	99	112	40.9	...	92.8	81.1	58.4	35.7	125	18
62	110	98	110	40.4	...	92.2	80.8	57.7	34.7	124	...
61	108	96	108	40.0	...	91.7	80.5	57.0	33.7	122	17
60	107	95	107	39.5	...	91.1	80.1	56.4	32.7	120	...
59	106	94	106	39.0	...	90.5	79.8	55.7	31.7	118	...
58	104	92	104	38.6	...	90.0	79.5	55.0	30.7	117	...
57	103	91	103	38.1	...	89.4	79.2	54.4	29.7	115	...
56	101	90	101	37.7	...	88.8	78.8	53.7	28.7	114	...
55	100	89	100	37.2	...	88.2	78.5	53.0	27.7	112	...

Note: Values in parentheses are beyond normal range and are given for information only.

(a) For carbon and alloy steels in the annealed, normalized, and quenched and tempered conditions; less accurate for cold worked condition and for austenitic steels

Source: **Metals Handbook, Mechanical Testing**, Vol. 8, 9th ed., ASM, 1985, p. 109-110

Approximate equivalent hardness numbers for Rockwell C hardness numbers for steel(a)

Rockwell hardness No.	Vickers hardness No.	Brinell hardness No., 3000-kg load, 10-mm ball Standard ball	Tungsten carbide ball	A scale, 60-kg load, diamond indenter	B scale, 100-kg load, 1/16-in.-diam ball	D scale, 100-kg load, diamond indenter	15N scale, 15-kg load	30N scale, 30-kg load	45N scale, 45-kg load	Knoop hardness No., 500-g load and greater	Scleroscope hardness No.
68	940	...	...	85.6	...	76.9	93.2	84.4	75.4	920	97
67	900	...	...	85.0	...	76.1	92.9	83.6	74.2	895	95
66	865	...	...	84.5	...	75.4	92.5	82.8	73.3	870	92
65	832	...	(739)	83.9	...	74.5	92.2	81.9	72.0	846	91
64	800	...	(722)	83.4	...	73.8	91.8	81.1	71.0	822	88
63	772	...	(705)	82.8	...	73.0	91.4	80.1	69.9	799	87
62	746	...	(688)	82.3	...	72.2	91.1	79.3	68.8	776	85
61	720	...	(670)	81.8	...	71.5	90.7	78.4	67.7	754	83
60	697	...	(654)	81.2	...	70.7	90.2	77.5	66.6	732	81
59	674	...	(634)	80.7	...	69.9	89.8	76.6	65.5	710	80
58	653	...	615	80.1	...	69.2	89.3	75.7	64.3	690	78
57	633	...	595	79.6	...	68.5	88.9	74.8	63.2	670	76
56	613	...	577	79.0	...	67.7	88.3	73.9	62.0	650	75
55	595	...	560	78.5	...	66.9	87.9	73.0	60.9	630	74
54	577	...	543	78.0	...	66.1	87.4	72.0	59.8	612	72
53	560	...	525	77.4	...	65.4	86.9	71.2	58.6	594	71
52	544	(500)	512	76.8	...	64.6	86.4	70.2	57.4	576	69
51	528	(487)	496	76.3	...	63.8	85.9	69.4	56.1	558	68
50	513	(475)	481	75.9	...	63.1	85.5	68.5	55.0	542	67
49	498	(464)	469	75.2	...	62.1	85.0	67.6	53.8	526	66
48	484	(451)	455	74.7	...	61.4	84.5	66.7	52.5	510	64
47	471	442	443	74.1	...	60.8	83.9	65.8	51.4	495	63
46	458	432	432	73.6	...	60.0	83.5	64.8	50.3	480	62
45	446	421	421	73.1	...	59.2	83.0	64.0	49.0	466	60
44	434	409	409	72.5	...	58.5	82.5	63.1	47.8	452	58
43	423	400	400	72.0	...	57.7	82.0	62.2	46.7	438	57
42	412	390	390	71.5	...	56.9	81.5	61.3	45.5	426	56
41	402	381	381	70.9	...	56.2	80.9	60.4	44.3	414	55
40	392	371	371	70.4	...	55.4	80.4	59.5	43.1	402	54
39	382	362	362	69.9	...	54.6	79.9	58.6	41.9	391	52
38	372	353	353	69.4	...	53.8	79.4	57.7	40.8	380	51
37	363	344	344	68.9	...	53.1	78.8	56.8	39.6	370	50
36	354	336	336	68.4	(109.0)	52.3	78.3	55.9	38.4	360	49
35	345	327	327	67.9	(108.5)	51.5	77.7	55.0	37.2	351	48
34	336	319	319	67.4	(108.0)	50.8	77.2	54.2	36.1	342	47
33	327	311	311	66.8	(107.5)	50.0	76.6	53.3	34.9	334	46
32	318	301	301	66.3	(107.0)	49.2	76.1	52.1	33.7	326	44
31	310	294	294	65.8	(106.0)	48.4	75.6	51.3	32.5	318	43
30	302	286	286	65.3	(105.5)	47.7	75.0	50.4	31.3	311	42
29	294	279	279	64.7	(104.5)	47.0	74.5	49.5	30.1	304	41
28	286	271	271	64.3	(104.0)	46.1	73.9	48.6	28.9	297	40
27	279	264	264	63.8	(103.0)	45.2	73.3	47.7	27.8	290	39
26	272	258	258	63.3	(102.5)	44.6	72.8	46.8	26.7	284	38
25	266	253	253	62.8	(101.5)	43.8	72.2	45.9	25.5	278	38
24	260	247	247	62.4	(101.0)	43.1	71.6	45.0	24.3	272	37
23	254	243	243	62.0	100.0	42.1	71.0	44.0	23.1	266	36
22	248	237	237	61.5	99.0	41.6	70.5	43.2	22.0	261	35
21	243	231	231	61.0	98.5	40.9	69.9	42.3	20.7	256	35

Note: Values in parentheses are beyond normal range and are given for information only.

(a) For carbon and alloy steels in the annealed, normalized, and quenched and tempered conditions; less accurate for cold worked condition and for austenitic steels

Source: *Metals Handbook, Mechanical Testing*, Vol. 8, 9th ed., ASM, 1985, p. 110

Approximate equivalent hardness numbers for Brinell hardness numbers for steel(a)

Brinell indentation diam, mm	Brinell hardness No. (b), 3000-kg load, 10-mm ball Standard ball	Tungsten carbide ball	Vickers hardness No.	A scale, 60-kg load, diamond indenter	B scale, 100-kg load, 1/16-in. diam ball	C scale, 150-kg load, diamond indenter	D scale, 100-kg load, diamond indenter	15N scale, 15-kg load	30N scale, 30-kg load	45N scale, 45-kg load	Knoop No., 500-g load and greater	Sclero-scope hardness No.
2.25	···	(745)	840	84.1	···	65.3	74.8	92.3	82.2	72.2	852	91
2.30	···	(712)	783	83.1	···	63.4	73.4	91.6	80.5	70.4	808	···
2.35	···	(682)	737	82.2	···	61.7	72.0	91.0	79.0	68.5	768	84
2.40	···	(653)	697	81.2	···	60.0	70.7	90.2	77.5	66.5	732	81
2.45	···	627	667	80.5	···	58.7	69.7	89.6	76.3	65.1	703	79
2.50	···	601	640	79.8	···	57.3	68.7	89.0	75.1	63.5	677	77
2.55	···	578	615	79.1	···	56.0	67.7	88.4	73.9	62.1	652	75
2.60	···	555	591	78.4	···	54.7	66.7	87.8	72.7	60.6	626	73
2.65	···	534	569	77.8	···	53.5	65.8	87.2	71.6	59.2	604	71
2.70	···	514	547	76.9	···	52.1	64.7	86.5	70.3	57.6	579	70
2.75	(495)	···	539	76.7	···	51.6	64.3	86.3	69.9	56.9	571	···
	···	495	528	76.3	···	51.0	63.8	85.9	69.4	56.1	558	68
2.80	(477)	···	516	75.9	···	50.3	63.2	85.6	68.7	55.2	545	···
	···	477	508	75.6	···	49.6	62.7	85.3	68.2	54.5	537	66
2.85	(461)	···	495	75.1	···	48.8	61.9	84.9	67.4	53.5	523	···
	···	461	491	74.9	···	48.5	61.7	84.7	67.2	53.2	518	65
2.90	444	···	474	74.3	···	47.2	61.0	84.1	66.0	51.7	499	···
	···	444	472	74.2	···	47.1	60.8	84.0	65.8	51.5	496	63
2.95	429	429	455	73.4	···	45.7	59.7	83.4	64.6	49.9	476	61
3.00	415	415	440	72.8	···	44.5	58.8	82.8	63.5	48.4	459	59
3.05	401	401	425	72.0	···	43.1	57.8	82.0	62.3	46.9	441	58
3.10	388	388	410	71.4	···	41.8	56.8	81.4	61.1	45.3	423	56
3.15	375	375	396	70.6	···	40.4	55.7	80.6	59.9	43.6	407	54
3.20	363	363	383	70.0	···	39.1	54.6	80.0	58.7	42.0	392	52
3.25	352	352	372	69.3	(110.0)	37.9	53.8	79.3	57.6	40.5	379	51
3.30	341	341	360	68.7	(109.0)	36.6	52.8	78.6	56.4	39.1	367	50
3.35	331	331	350	68.1	(108.5)	35.5	51.9	78.0	55.4	37.8	356	48
3.40	321	321	339	67.5	(108.0)	34.3	51.0	77.3	54.3	36.4	345	47
3.45	311	311	328	66.9	(107.5)	33.1	50.0	76.7	53.3	34.4	336	46
3.50	302	302	319	66.3	(107.0)	32.1	49.3	76.1	52.2	33.8	327	45
3.55	293	293	309	65.7	(106.0)	30.9	48.3	75.5	51.2	32.4	318	43
3.60	285	285	301	65.3	(105.5)	29.9	47.6	75.0	50.3	31.2	310	42
3.65	277	277	292	64.6	(104.5)	28.8	46.7	74.4	49.3	29.9	302	41
3.70	269	269	284	64.1	(104.0)	27.6	45.9	73.7	48.3	28.5	294	40
3.75	262	262	276	63.6	(103.0)	26.6	45.0	73.1	47.3	27.3	286	39
3.80	255	255	269	63.0	(102.0)	25.4	44.2	72.5	46.2	26.0	279	38
3.85	248	248	261	62.5	(101.0)	24.2	43.2	71.7	45.1	24.5	272	37
3.90	241	241	253	61.8	100.0	22.8	42.0	70.9	43.9	22.8	265	36
3.95	235	235	247	61.4	99.0	21.7	41.4	70.3	42.9	21.5	259	35
4.00	229	229	241	60.8	98.2	20.5	40.5	69.7	41.9	20.1	253	34
4.05	223	223	234	···	97.3	(19.0)	···	···	···	···	247	···
4.10	217	217	228	···	96.4	(17.7)	···	···	···	···	242	33
4.15	212	212	222	···	95.5	(16.4)	···	···	···	···	237	32
4.20	207	207	218	···	94.6	(15.2)	···	···	···	···	232	31
4.25	201	201	212	···	93.7	(13.8)	···	···	···	···	227	···
4.30	197	197	207	···	92.8	(12.7)	···	···	···	···	222	30
4.35	192	192	202	···	91.9	(11.5)	···	···	···	···	217	29
4.40	187	187	196	···	90.9	(10.2)	···	···	···	···	212	···
4.45	183	183	192	···	90.0	(9.0)	···	···	···	···	207	28
4.50	179	179	188	···	89.0	(8.0)	···	···	···	···	202	27
4.55	174	174	182	···	88.0	(6.7)	···	···	···	···	198	···
4.60	170	170	178	···	87.0	(5.4)	···	···	···	···	194	26
4.65	167	167	175	···	86.0	(4.4)	···	···	···	···	190	···
4.70	163	163	171	···	85.0	(3.3)	···	···	···	···	186	25
4.75	159	159	167	···	83.9	(2.0)	···	···	···	···	182	···
4.80	156	156	163	···	82.9	(0.9)	···	···	···	···	178	24
4.85	152	152	159	···	81.9	···	···	···	···	···	174	···
4.90	149	149	156	···	80.8	···	···	···	···	···	170	23
4.95	146	146	153	···	79.7	···	···	···	···	···	166	···
5.00	143	143	150	···	78.6	···	···	···	···	···	163	22
5.10	137	137	143	···	76.4	···	···	···	···	···	157	21
5.20	131	131	137	···	74.2	···	···	···	···	···	151	···
5.30	126	126	132	···	72.0	···	···	···	···	···	145	20
5.40	121	121	127	···	69.8	···	···	···	···	···	140	19
5.50	116	116	122	···	67.6	···	···	···	···	···	135	18
5.60	111	111	117	···	65.4	···	···	···	···	···	131	17

Note: Values in parentheses are beyond normal range and are given for information only.
(a) For carbon and alloy steels in the annealed, normalized, and quenched and tempered conditions; less accurate for cold worked

condition and for austenitic steels. (b) Brinell numbers are based on the diameter of impressed indentation. If the ball distorts (flattens) during the test, Brinell numbers will vary in accordance with the degree of such distortion when related to hardnesses determined with a Vickers diamond pyramid, Rockwell diamond indenter, or other indenter that does not sensibly distort. At high hardnesses, therefore, the relationship between Brinell and Vickers or Rockwell scales is affected by the type of ball used. Standard steel balls tend to flatten slightly more than tungsten carbide balls, resulting in a larger indentation and a lower Brinell number than shown by a tungsten carbide ball. Thus, on a specimen of about 539 to 547 HV, a standard ball will leave a 2.75-mm indentation (495 HB) and a tungsten carbide ball a 2.70-mm indentation (514 HB). Conversely, identical indentation diameters for both types of balls will correspond to different Vickers and Rockwell values. Thus, if indentations in two different specimens are both 2.75 mm in diameter (495 HB), the specimen tested with a standard ball has a Vickers hardness of 539, whereas the specimen tested with a tungsten carbide ball has a Vickers hardness of 528.

Source: **Metals Handbook, Mechanical Testing**, Vol. 8, 9th ed., ASM, 1985, p. 111

Approximate equivalent hardness numbers for Vickers (diamond pyramid) hardness numbers for steel(a)

Vickers hardness No.	Brinell hardness No., 3000-kg load, 10-mm ball		Rockwell hardness No.:				Rockwell superficial (diamond pyramid) hardness No.. diamond indenter			Knoop hardness No., 500-g load and greater	Sclero-scope hardness No.
	Standard ball	Tungsten carbide ball	A scale, 60-kg load, diamond indenter	B scale, 100-kg load, 1/16-in.- diam ball	C scale, 150-kg load, diamond indenter	D scale, 100-kg load, diamond indenter	15N scale, 15-kg load	30N scale, 30-kg load	45N scale, 45-kg load		
940	...	...	85.6	...	68.0	76.9	93.2	84.4	75.4	920	97
920	...	...	85.3	...	67.5	76.5	93.0	84.0	74.8	908	96
900	...	...	85.0	...	67.0	76.1	92.9	83.6	74.2	895	95
880	...	(767)	84.7	...	66.4	75.7	92.7	83.1	73.6	882	93
860	...	(757)	84.4	...	65.9	75.3	92.5	82.7	73.1	867	92
840	...	(745)	84.1	...	65.3	74.8	92.3	82.2	72.2	852	91
820	...	(733)	83.8	...	64.7	74.3	92.1	81.7	71.8	837	90
800	...	(722)	83.4	...	64.0	73.8	91.8	81.1	71.0	822	88
780	...	(710)	83.0	...	63.3	73.3	91.5	80.4	70.2	806	87
760	...	(698)	82.6	...	62.5	72.6	91.2	79.7	69.4	788	86
740	...	(684)	82.2	...	61.8	72.1	91.0	79.1	68.6	772	84
720	...	(670)	81.8	...	61.0	71.5	90.7	78.4	67.7	754	83
700	...	(656)	81.3	...	60.1	70.8	90.3	77.6	66.7	735	81
690	...	(647)	81.1	...	59.7	70.5	90.1	77.2	66.2	725	...
680	...	(638)	80.8	...	59.2	70.1	89.8	76.8	65.7	716	80
670	...	(630)	80.6	...	58.8	69.8	89.7	76.4	65.3	706	...
660	...	620	80.3	...	58.3	69.4	89.5	75.9	64.7	697	79
650	...	611	80.0	...	57.8	69.0	89.2	75.5	64.1	687	78

Note: Values in parentheses are beyond normal range and are given for information only.

(a) For carbon and alloy steels in the annealed, normalized, and quenched and tempered conditions; less accurate for cold worked condition and for austenitic steels.

Source: **Metals Handbook, Mechanical Testing**, Vol. 8, 9th ed., ASM, 1985, p. 112-113

Approximate equivalent hardness numbers for Vickers (diamond pyramid) hardness numbers for steel (continued)(a)

Vickers hardness No.	Brinell hardness No., 3000-kg load, 10-mm ball Standard ball	Tungsten carbide ball	Rockwell hardness No. A scale, 60-kg load, diamond indenter	B scale, 100-kg load, 1/16-in.-diam ball	C scale, 150-kg load, diamond indenter	D scale, 100-kg load, diamond indenter	Rockwell superficial (diamond pyramid) hardness No., diamond indenter 15N scale, 15-kg load	30N scale, 30-kg load	45N scale, 45-kg load	Knoop hardness No., 500-g load and greater	Scleroscope hardness No.
640	...	601	79.8	...	57.3	68.7	89.0	75.1	63.5	677	77
630	...	591	79.5	...	56.8	68.3	88.8	74.6	63.0	667	76
620	...	582	79.2	...	56.3	67.9	88.5	74.2	62.4	657	75
610	...	573	78.9	...	55.7	67.5	88.2	73.6	61.7	646	...
600	...	564	78.6	...	55.2	67.0	88.0	73.2	61.2	636	74
590	...	554	78.4	...	54.7	66.7	87.8	72.7	60.5	625	73
580	...	545	78.0	...	54.1	66.2	87.5	72.1	59.9	615	72
570	...	535	77.8	...	53.6	65.8	87.2	71.7	59.3	604	...
560	...	525	77.4	...	53.0	65.4	86.9	71.2	58.6	594	71
550	(505)	517	77.0	...	52.3	64.8	86.6	70.5	57.8	583	70
540	(496)	507	76.7	...	51.7	64.4	86.3	70.0	57.0	572	69
530	(488)	497	76.4	...	51.1	63.9	86.0	69.5	56.2	561	68
520	(480)	488	76.1	...	50.5	63.5	85.7	69.0	55.6	550	67
510	(473)	479	75.7	...	49.8	62.9	85.4	68.3	54.7	539	...
500	(465)	471	75.3	...	49.1	62.2	85.0	67.7	53.9	528	66
490	(456)	460	74.9	...	48.4	61.6	84.7	67.1	53.1	517	65
480	(448)	452	74.5	...	47.7	61.3	84.3	66.4	52.2	505	64
470	441	442	74.1	...	46.9	60.7	83.9	65.7	51.3	494	...
460	433	433	73.6	...	46.1	60.1	83.6	64.9	50.4	482	62
450	425	425	73.3	...	45.3	59.4	83.2	64.3	49.4	471	...
440	415	415	72.8	...	44.5	58.8	82.8	63.5	48.4	459	59
430	405	405	72.3	...	43.6	58.2	82.3	62.7	47.4	447	58
420	397	397	71.8	...	42.7	57.5	81.8	61.9	46.4	435	57
410	388	388	71.4	...	41.8	56.8	81.4	61.1	45.3	423	56
400	379	379	70.8	...	40.8	56.0	80.8	60.2	44.1	412	55
390	369	369	70.3	...	39.8	55.2	80.3	59.3	42.9	400	...
380	360	360	69.8	(110.0)	38.8	54.4	79.8	58.4	41.7	389	52
370	350	350	69.2	...	37.7	53.6	79.2	57.4	40.4	378	51
360	341	341	68.7	(109.0)	36.6	52.8	78.6	56.4	39.1	367	50
350	331	331	68.1	...	35.5	51.9	78.0	55.4	37.8	356	48
340	322	322	67.6	(108.0)	34.4	51.1	77.4	54.4	36.5	346	47
330	313	313	67.0	...	33.3	50.2	76.8	53.6	35.2	337	46
320	303	303	66.4	(107.0)	32.2	49.4	76.2	52.3	33.9	328	45
310	294	294	65.8	...	31.0	48.4	75.6	51.3	32.5	318	...
300	284	284	65.2	(105.5)	29.8	47.5	74.9	50.2	31.1	309	42
295	280	280	64.8	...	29.2	47.1	74.6	49.7	30.4	305	...
290	275	275	64.5	(104.5)	28.5	46.5	74.2	49.0	29.5	300	41
285	270	270	64.2	...	27.8	46.0	73.8	48.4	28.7	296	...
280	265	265	63.8	(103.5)	27.1	45.3	73.4	47.8	27.9	291	40
275	261	261	63.5	...	26.4	44.9	73.0	47.2	27.1	286	39
270	256	256	63.1	(102.0)	25.6	44.3	72.6	46.4	26.2	282	38
265	252	252	62.7	...	24.8	43.7	72.1	45.7	25.2	277	...
260	247	247	62.4	(101.0)	24.0	43.1	71.6	45.0	24.3	272	37
255	243	243	62.0	...	23.1	42.2	71.1	44.2	23.2	267	...
250	238	238	61.6	99.5	22.2	41.7	70.6	43.4	22.2	262	36
245	233	233	61.2	...	21.3	41.1	70.1	42.5	21.1	258	35
240	228	228	60.7	98.1	20.3	40.3	69.6	41.7	19.9	253	34
230	219	219	...	96.7	(18.0)	...	...	...	...	243	33
220	209	209	...	95.0	(15.7)	...	...	...	...	234	32
210	200	200	...	93.4	(13.4)	...	...	...	...	226	30
200	190	190	...	91.5	(11.0)	...	...	...	...	216	29
190	181	181	...	89.5	(8.5)	...	...	...	...	206	28
180	171	171	...	87.1	(6.0)	...	...	...	...	196	26
170	162	162	...	85.0	(3.0)	...	...	...	...	185	25
160	152	152	...	81.7	(0.0)	...	...	...	...	175	23
150	143	143	...	78.7	...	...	...	...	...	164	22
140	133	133	...	75.0	...	...	...	...	...	154	21
130	124	124	...	71.2	...	...	...	...	...	143	20
120	114	114	...	66.7	...	...	...	...	...	133	18
110	105	105	...	62.3	...	...	...	...	...	123	...
100	95	95	...	56.2	...	...	...	...	...	112	...
95	90	90	...	52.0	...	...	...	...	...	107	...
90	86	86	...	48.0	...	...	...	...	...	102	...
85	81	81	...	41.0	...	...	...	...	...	97	...

Note: Values in parentheses are beyond normal range and are given for information only.
(a) For carbon and alloy steels in the annealed, normalized, and quenched and tempered conditions; less accurate for cold worked condition and for austenitic steels.

Appendix 2 Metric and Conversion Data

This Appendix is intended as a guide for expressing weights and measures in the Systeme International d'Unites (SI) for use in mechanical testing. The purpose of SI units, developed and maintained by the General Conference of Weights and Measures, is to provide a basis for worldwide standardization of units and measure. For more information on metric conversions, the reader should consult the following references:

- "Standard for Metric Practice," E 380, ASTM, Philadelphia, 1984

- "Metric Practice," ANSI/IEEE 268-1982, American National Standards Institute, New York, 1982

- *Metric Practice Guide--Units and Conversion Factors for the Steel Industry,* American Iron and Steel Institute, Washington, 1978

- *The International System of Units,* SP 330, National Bureau of Standards, Washington, 1981

- *Metric Editorial Guide,* 4th ed., American National Metric Council, Washington, 1984

- *ASME Orientation and Guide for Use of SI (Metric) Units,* ASME Guide SI 1, 9th ed., The American Society of Mechanical Engineers, New York, 1982

Base, supplementary, and derived SI units

Measure	Unit	Symbol
Base units		
Amount of substance . . . . mole		mol
Electric current . . . . ampere		A
Length . . . . meter		m
Luminous intensity . . . . candela		cd
Mass . . . . kilogram		kg
Thermodynamic temperature . . . . . . kelvin		K
Time . . . . second		s
Supplementary units		
Plane angle . . . . radian		rad
Solid angle . . . . steradian		sr
Derived units		
Absorbed dose . . . . gray		Gy
Acceleration . . . . meter per second squared		m/s^2
Activity (of radionuclides) . . . . becquerel		Bq
Angular acceleration . . . . radian per second squared		rad/s^2
Angular velocity . . . . radian per second		rad/s
Area . . . . square meter		m^2
Capacitance . . . . farad		F
Concentration (of amount		
of substance) . . . . mole per cubic meter		mol/m^3
Conductance . . . . siemens		S
Current density . . . . ampere per square meter		A/m^2
Density, mass . . . . kilogram per cubic meter		kg/m^3
Electric charge density . . . . coulomb per cubic meter		C/m^3
Electric field strength . . . . volt per meter		V/m
Electric flux density . . . . coulomb per square meter		C/m^2
Electric potential, potential		
difference, electromotive force . . volt		V
Electric resistance . . . . ohm		Ω
Energy, work, quantity of heat . . . . joule		J
Energy density . . . . joule per cubic meter		J/m^3
Entropy . . . . joule per kelvin		J/K
Force . . . . newton		N
Frequency . . . . hertz		Hz
Heat capacity . . . . joule per kelvin		J/K
Heat flux density . . . . watt per square meter		W/m^2
Illuminance . . . . lux		lx
Inductance . . . . henry		H
Irradiance . . . . watt per square meter		W/m^2
Luminance . . . . candela per square meter		cd/m^2
Luminous flux . . . . lumen		lm
Magnetic field strength . . . . ampere per meter		A/m
Magnetic flux . . . . weber		WB
Magnetic flux density . . . . tesla		T
Molar energy . . . . joule per mole		J/mol
Molar entropy . . . . joule per mole kelvin		J/mol $\cdot$ K
Molar heat capacity . . . . joule per mole kelvin		J/mol $\cdot$ K
Moment of force . . . . newton meter		N $\cdot$ m
Permeability . . . . henry per meter		H/m
Permittivity . . . . farad per meter		F/m
Power, radiant flux . . . . watt		W
Pressure, stress . . . . pascal		Pa
Quantity of electricity,		
electric charge . . . . coulomb		C

Source: **Metals Handbook, Mechanical Testing,** *Vol. 8, 9th ed., ASM, 1985, p. 721*

Base, supplementary, and derived SI units (continued)

Measure	Unit	Symbol
Radiance	watt per square meter steradian	$W/m^2 \cdot sr$
Radiant intensity	watt per steradian	W/sr
Specific heat capacity	joule per kilogram kelvin	$J/kg \cdot K$
Specific energy	joule per kilogram	J/kg
Specific entropy	joule per kilogram kelvin	$J/kg \cdot K$
Specific volume	cubic meter per kilogram	m^3/kg
Surface tension	newton per meter	N/m
Thermal conductivity	watt per meter kelvin	$W/m \cdot K$
Velocity	meter per second	m/s
Viscosity, dynamic	pascal second	$Pa \cdot s$
Viscosity, kinematic	square meter per second	m^2/s
Volume	cubic meter	m^3
Wavenumber	1 per meter	$1/m$

Source: Metals Handbook, Mechanical Testing, Vol. 8, 9th ed., ASM, 1985, p. 721

SI prefixes--names and symbols

Exponential expression	Multiplication factor	Prefix	Symbol
10^{18}	1 000 000 000 000 000 000	exa	E
10^{15}	1 000 000 000 000 000	peta	P
10^{12}	1 000 000 000 000	tera	T
10^{9}	1 000 000 000	giga	G
10^{6}	1 000 000	mega	M
10^{3}	1 000	kilo	K
10^{2}	100	hecto(a)	h
10^{1}	10	deka(a)	da
10^{0}	1	BASE UNIT	
10^{-1}	0.1	deci(a)	d
10^{-2}	0.01	centi(a)	c
10^{-3}	0.001	milli	m
10^{-6}	0.000 001	micro	μ
10^{-9}	0.000 000 001	nano	n
10^{-12}	0.000 000 000 001	pico	p
10^{-15}	0.000 000 000 000 001	femto	f
10^{-18}	0.000 000 000 000 000 001	atto	a

(a) Nonpreferred. Prefixes should be selected in steps of 10^3, so that the resultant number before the prefix is between 0.1 and 1000. These prefixes should not be used for units of linear measurement, but may be used for higher order units. For example, the linear measurement decimeter is nonpreferred, but square decimeter is acceptable.
Source: **Metals Handbook, Mechanical Testing**, Vol. 8, 9th ed., ASM, 1985, p. 722

Conversion factors

To convert from	to	multiply by
Angle		
degree	rad	1.745 329 E − 02
Area		
in.^{2}	mm^2	6.451 600 E + 02
in.^{2}	cm^2	6.451 600 E + 00
in.^{2}	m^2	6.451 600 E − 04
ft^2	m^2	9.290 304 E − 02
Bending moment or torque		
lbf · in.	N · m	1.129 848 E − 01
lbf · ft	N · m	1.355 818 E + 00
kgf · m	N · m	9.806 650 E + 00
ozf · in.	N · m	7.061 552 E − 03
Bending moment or torque per unit length		
lbf · in./in.	N · m/m	4.448 222 E + 00
lbf · ft/in.	N · m/m	5.337 866 E + 01
Current density		
A/in.^{2}	A/mm^2	1.550 003 E − 03
A/ft^2	A/m^2	1.076 400 E + 01

To convert from	to	multiply by
Electricity and magnetism		
gauss	T	1.000 000 E − 04
maxwell	μWb	1.000 000 E − 02
mho	S	1.000 000 E + 00
Oersted	A/m	7.957 700 E + 01
Ω · cm	Ω · m	1.000 000 E − 02
Ω circular-mil/ft	μΩ · m	1.662 426 E − 03
Energy (impact, other)		
ft · lbf	J	1.355 818 E + 00
Btu (thermochemical)	J	1.054 350 E + 03
cal (thermochemical)	J	4.184 000 E + 00
kW · h	J	3.600 000 E + 06
W · h	J	3.600 000 E + 03
Flow rate		
ft^3/h	L/min	4.719 475 E − 01
ft^3/min	L/min	2.831 000 E + 01
gal/h	L/min	6.309 020 E − 02
gal/min	L/min	3.785 412 E + 00

Source: **Metals Handbook, Mechanical Testing**, Vol. 8, 9th ed., ASM, 1985, p. 722-723

Conversion factors (continued)

To convert from	to	multiply by
Force		
lbf	N	4.448 222 E + 00
kip (1000 lbf)	N	4.448 222 E + 03
tonf	kN	8.896 443 E + 00
kgf	N	9.806 650 E + 00
Force per unit length		
lbf/ft	N/m	1.459 390 E + 01
lbf/in.	N/m	1.751 268 E + 02
Fracture toughness		
ksi$\sqrt{\text{in.}}$	MPa$\sqrt{\text{m}}$	1.098 800 E + 00
Heat content		
Btu/lb	kJ/kg	2.326 000 E + 00
cal/g	kJ/kg	4.186 800 E + 00
Heat input		
J/in.	J/m	3.937 008 E + 01
kJ/in.	kJ/m	3.937 008 E + 01
Length		
Å	nm	1.000 000 E − 01
μin.	μm	2.540 000 E − 02
mil	μm	2.540 000 E + 01
in.	mm	2.540 000 E + 01
in.	cm	2.540 000 E + 00
ft	m	3.048 000 E − 01
yd	m	9.144 000 E − 01
mile	km	1.609 300 E + 00
Mass		
oz	kg	2.834 952 E − 02
lb	kg	4.535 924 E − 01
ton (short, 2000 lb)	kg	9.071 847 E + 02
ton (short, 2000 lb)	kg × 10^3(a)	9.071 847 E − 01
ton (long, 2240 lb)	kg	1.016 047 E + 03
Mass per unit area		
oz/in.^{2}	kg/m^2	4.395 000 E + 01
oz/ft^2	kg/m^2	3.051 517 E − 01
oz/yd^2	kg/m^2	3.390 575 E − 02
lb/ft^2	kg/m^2	4.882 428 E + 00
Mass per unit length		
lb/ft	kg/m	1.488 164 E + 00
lb/in.	kg/m	1.785 797 E + 01
Mass per unit time		
lb/h	kg/s	1.259 979 E − 04
lb/min	kg/s	7.559 873 E − 03
lb/s	kg/s	4.535 924 E − 01

To convert from	to	multiply by
Mass per unit volume (includes density)		
g/cm^3	kg/m^3	1.000 000 E + 03
lb/ft^3	g/cm^3	1.601 846 E − 02
lb/ft^3	kg/m^3	1.601 846 E + 01
lb/in.^{3}	g/cm^3	2.767 990 E + 01
lb/in.^{3}	kg/m^3	2.767 990 E + 04
Power		
Btu/s	kW	1.055 056 E + 00
Btu/min	kW	1.758 426 E − 02
Btu/h	W	2.928 751 E − 01
erg/s	W	1.000 000 E − 07
ft · lbf/s	W	1.355 818 E + 00
ft · lbf/min	W	2.259 697 E − 02
ft · lbf/h	W	3.766 161 E − 04
hp (550 ft · lbf/s)	kW	7.456 999 E − 01
hp (electric)	kW	7.460 000 E − 01
Power density		
W/in.^{2}	W/m^2	1.550 003 E + 03
Pressure (fluid)		
atm (standard)	Pa	1.013 250 E + 05
bar	Pa	1.000 000 E + 05
in.Hg (32 °F)	Pa	3.386 380 E + 03
in.Hg (60 °F)	Pa	3.376 850 E + 03
lbf/in.^{2} (psi)	Pa	6.894 757 E + 03
torr (mmHg, 0 °C)	Pa	1.333 220 E + 02
Specific heat		
Btu/lb · °F	J/kg · K	4.186 800 E + 03
cal/g · °C	J/kg · K	4.186 800 E + 03
Stress (force per unit area)		
tonf/in.^{2} (tsi)	MPa	1.378 951 E + 01
kgf/mm^2	MPa	9.806 650 E + 00
Stress (force per unit area)		
ksi	MPa	6.894 757 E + 00
lbf/in.^{2} (psi)	MPa	6.894 757 E − 03
MN/m^2	MPa	1.000 000 E + 00
Temperature		
°F	°C	5/9 · (°F − 32)
°R	°K	5/9
Temperature interval		
°F	°C	5/9
Thermal conductivity		
Btu · in./s · ft^2 · °F	W/m · K	5.192 204 E + 02
Btu/ft · h · °F	W/m · K	1.730 735 E + 00
Btu · in./h · ft^2 · °F	W/m · K	1.442 279 E − 01
cal/cm · s · °C	W/m · K	4.184 000 E + 02

(a) kg x 10^3 = 1 metric ton

Source: Metals Handbook, Mechanical Testing, Vol. 8, 9th ed., ASM, 1985, p. 722-723

Conversion factors (continued)

To convert from	to	multiply by
Thermal expansion		
in./in. · °C	m/m · K	1.000 000 E + 00
in./in. · °F	m/m · K	1.800 000 E + 00
Velocity		
ft/h	m/s	8.466 667 E − 05
ft/min	m/s	5.080 000 E − 03
ft/s	m/s	3.048 000 E − 01
in./s	m/s	2.540 000 E − 02
km/h	m/s	2.777 778 E − 01
mph	km/h	1.609 344 E + 00
Velocity of rotation		
rev/min (rpm)	rad/s	1.047 164 E − 01
rev/s	rad/s	6.283 185 E + 00
Viscosity		
poise	Pa · s	1.000 000 E + 01

To convert from	to	multiply by
strokes	m^2/s	1.000 000 E − 04
ft^2/s	m^2/s	9.290 304 E − 02
$in.^2/s$	mm^2/s	6.451 600 E + 02
Volume		
$in.^3$	m^3	1.638 706 E − 05
ft^3	m^3	2.831 685 E − 02
fluid oz	m^3	2.957 353 E − 05
gal (U.S. liquid)	m^3	3.785 412 E − 03
Volume per unit time		
ft^3/min	m^3/s	4.719 474 E − 04
ft^3/s	m^3/s	2.831 685 E − 02
$in.^3/min$	m^3/s	2.731 177 E − 07
Wavelength		
Å	nm	1.000 000 E − 01

*Source: **Metals Handbook, Mechanical Testing**, Vol. 8, 9th ed., ASM, 1985, p. 722-723*

Appendix 3 Directory of Equipment Manufacturers and Suppliers in the United States

Company/Phone No.	Address	Comments[a]
American SIP Corp. (914) 592-8006	530 Saw Mill River Rd. Elmsford, NY 10523	M, D
American Stress Technologies, Inc. (412) 854-0789	515 Hollydale Dr. Bethel Park, PA 15102	M, D: portable testers
Ames Precision Machine Works (313) 483-4238	5270 Geddes Rd. Ann Arbor, MI 48105	M
AOR Inc. (215) 675-2510	P.O. Box 429 Willow Grove, PA 19090	D, S: testers (Rockwell, Brinell, Microhardness, Knoop, Vickers, portable and automated systems for production hardness testing)
AT&T Nondestructive Testing Systems (800) 424-4241	1 Executive Dr. Somerset, NJ 08873	M
Automation Engineering, Inc. (901) 382-5544	1691 Shelby Oaks N #4 Memphis, TN 38134	M: Rockwell Testers and automatic hardness testers based on Rockwell scales
Frank Bacon Machine Sales Co. (313) 756-4280	4433 E. Eight Mile Rd. P.O. Box 886-AM Warren, MI 48090-0886	D: new and rebuilt testers Rockwell, Brinell, Micro-, hardness, Knoop, Vickers, and portable)
Edwin H. Benz Co. Inc. (401) 331-5650	73 Maplehurst Ave. Providence, RI 02908	D: testers (Rockwell, portable and Durometers)

[a] M = manufacture, D = distribute, S = service

Company/Phone No.	Address	Comments[a]
Buehler, Ltd. (312) 295-6500	41 Waukegan Rd. Lake Bluff, IL 60044	M, D, S: testers (Rockwell, Brinell, Microhardness, Knoop, Vickers, and portable)
Certified Testing Laboratories Inc. (212) 824-1616	2623 Roberts Ave. Bronx, NY 10461	D
Clark Instrument, Inc. (313) 769-5560	145 Enterprise Dr. Ann Arbor, MI 48105	M, D, S: testers (Rockwell, Brinell, Microhardness, Knoop, Vickers, and Portable)
CMS Systems, Inc. (206) 653-9844	11132 46th Dr. N.E. Marysville, WA 09270	D: testers (Rockwell, Brinell, Vickers, and portable)
Cosco-Colorado Scientific Instrument & Supply Co. (303) 832-2811	Div. of Wexco Intl.Corp 900 Broadway Denver, CO 80203	D
Detroit Testing Machine Co. (313) 921-0659	9390 Grinnell Ave. Detroit, MI 48213	M, D, S: Brinell and portable testers
Dimensions Div. Radiation Equipment Co. Inc. (312) 831-2900	1495 Old Deerfield Rd. Highland Park IL 60035	D, S: testers (Rockwell, Brinell, Microhardness, Vickers, and portables; and distributes Scleroscopes and Durometers)
Doall (312) 824-1122	254 N. Laurel Ave. Des Plaines, IL 60016	D: testers (Rockwell, Brinell, and portable)
Eastern NDT, Inc. (804) 458-1661	200 N. Main St. Suite 212 Hopewell, VA 23860	D
Electromatic Equipment Co. Inc. (516) 295-4300	600 Oakland Ave. Cedarhurst, NY 11516	D: portable testers and Durometers
Elektro-Physik USA Inc. (312) 437-6616 (800) 782-1506	778 Algonquin Arlington Heights IL 60005	D: Microhardness testers and Durometers
Excel Technologies Inc. (203) 741-3435	99 Phoenix Ave. Enfield, CT 06082	D

[a] M = manufacture, D = distribute, S = service

Company/Phone No.	Address	Comments[a]
Dietert Division of Geo. Fischer Foundry Systems Inc. (313) 634-8251	407 Hadley St. P.O. Box 50 Holly, MI 48442	M, D, S: portable testers for mold strength and surface hardness
Fred V. Fowler Co. Inc. (617) 332-7004	66 Rowe St. Newton, MA 02166	D
Furnace Brokers, Inc. (203) 875-3712	P.O. Box 774 98 E. Main St. Vernon, CT 06066	D
Paul N. Gardner Co. Inc. (305) 946-9454	316 Northeast First St. Pompano Beach FL 33060	D, S: testers (Rockwell, Brinell portable and Durometers, and hardness testers for paints and coatings)
Gogan Machine Corp. (216) 431-3941	1440 E. 55th St. Cleveland, OH 44103	M, D, S: Gogan hardness testers (Brinell scales)
Hacker Instruments Inc. (201) 226-8450	Box 657 Fairfield, NJ 07007	M, D
Halem Sales & Service Co. (805) 522-2131	P.O. Box 358 Simi Valley, CA 93062	D, S: testers (Rockwell, Brinell, Microhardness, Knoop, Vickers, and portable)
Hentschel Instruments, Inc. (313) 973-2505	P.O. Box 981 Ann Arbor MI 48106-0981	D, S: portable testers
Hi-Heat Company Inc. 203) 528-9315	1330B Main Street E. Hartford, CT 06108	D: Rockwell and Microhardness testers
Hocking NDT, Inc. (301) 449-6400	6807 Coolridge Dr. Temple Hills, MD 20748	M
Hutchison-Hayes Int'l (713) 452-0222	P.O. Box 2965 Houston, TX 77252	M, D, S: Rockwell testers
Industronics, Inc. (203) 289-1588	489 Sullivan Ave S. Windsor, CT 06074	D
King Tester Corp. (215) 279-6010	510 Feheley Dr. King of Prussia PA 19406	M
Krautkramer Branson (717) 242-0327	P.O. Box 350 Lewistown, PA 17044	M, D, S: Microdur ultrasonic portable microhardness tester (Rockwell B, C, and Vickers equivalent readout)

[a] M = manufacture, D = distribute, S = service

Company/Phone No.	Address	Comments[a]
K.J. Law Engineers Inc. (313) 478-3150	23660 Research Drive Farmington Hills, MI 48024	M, S: testers (Rockwell, Brinell, and automated systems)
Leco Corporation (616) 983-5531	3000 Lakeview Ave. St. Joseph, MI 49085-2396	D, S: testers (Rockwell, Brinell, Microhardness, Knoop, and Vickers)
E. Leitz Inc. (201) 767-1100	24 Link Dr. Rockleigh, NJ 07647	M, D
Mager Scientific MI (313) 662-1472 Other (800) 521-8768	P.O. Box 160 Dexter, MI 48130	D: testers (Rockwell, Brinell, Microhardness, Knoop and Vickers
Mager Scientific (612) 633-6884	547-17 Avenue NW New Brighton MN 55112	D: testers (Rockwell, Brinell, Microhardness, Knoop, Vickers, and portable)
Mark V Laboratory Inc. (203) 653-7201	P.O. Box 310 18 Kripes Rd. E. Granby, CT 06026	M, D: testers (Rockwell, Brinell, Microhardness, Vickers, portable, and Scleroscope)
E. McGrath Inc. (617) 744-3546	35 Osborne St. Salem, MA 01970	D
T.R. McKee & Assoc. (713) 324-1088	1502 Running Bear Tr. Crosby, TX 77532	D: testers (Rockwell, Brinell, Microhardness, Knoop, Vickers, and portables)
Metlab Corporation (716) 282-6950	P.O. Box 1075 1517 Main St. Niagara Falls NY 14302	D, S: testers (Rockwell, Brinell, Microhardness, Knoop, Vickers, portable, Scleroscopes, Durometers, and dynamic hardness)
Metallurgical Supply Co. Inc. (713) 481-4100	923 F.M. Rd. 1959 Houston, TX 77034	D, S: testers (Rockwell, Brinell, Microhardness, Vickers, portable, Scleroscopes, and Durometers)
Michigan NDT Inc. (313) 475-2979	P.O. Box 296 Chelsea, MI 48118	D: testers (Rockwell and Brinell)
The Microscope Co. Inc. (216) 237-9800	13800 Progress Pkwy. Suite B Cleveland, OH 44133	D, S: testers (Rockwell, Brinell, Microhardness, Knoop, Vickers, portable, Scleroscopes, and Durometers)
M-P-M Products Co. (801) 466-8776	375 W. Gregson Ave. Salt Lake, UT 84115	D, S: testers (Rockwell, Brinell, Microhardness, Vickers, portable, Scleroscopes and Durometers) services Rockwell, Brinell, and portable

[a] M = manufacture, D = distribute, S = service

Company/Phone No.	Address	Comments[a]
M-R Equipment Corp. (216) 883-4335	7401 Morgan Ave. Cleveland, OH 44127	D: testers (Rockwell and Brinell)
Newage Industries, Inc. (215) 657-6040	2300 Maryland Rd. Willow Grove PA 19090	M, D: testers (Rockwell, Brinell, Microhardness, Vickers, and portables), calibration devices, and test blocks
New England Calibration Div. D.L. Ellis Co. Inc. (617) 263-2298	P.O. Box 592 Acton, MA 01720	D, S: testers (Rockwell, Brinell, Microhardness, Knoop, Vickers, portable, Scleroscopes, and Durometers)
New York Calibration Div. D.L. Ellis Co. Inc. (315) 732-6154	P.O. Box 4353 Utica, NY 13504	D, S: testers (Rockwell, Brinell, Microhardness, Knoop, Vickers, portable, Scleroscopes and Durometers)
Nikon Inc. Instrument Group (516) 222-0200	623 Stewart Avenue Garden City NY 11530	M, D, S: high-temperature Microhardness testers
Opti-Met Laboratories Inc. (617) 527-8253	P.O. Box 103 Newton, MA 02168	D: testers (Rockwell, Microhardness, Knoop, and Vickers)
Pacific Transducer Corp. (213) 478-1134	2301 Federal Ave. Los Angeles, CA 90064	M, D, S: testers (Rockwell (equivalent), Brinell, Microhardness, portable, Durometers); services portable testers and Durometers
Page-Wilson Corp. Measurement Syst. Div. (203) 335-2511	929 Connecticut Ave. Bridgeport, CT 06602	M, D, S: testers (Rockwell, Brinell, Microhardness, Knoop, Vickers, portable); distributes Rockwell, Brinell, and portable
Patriot Manufacturing Div. D.L. Ellis Co. Inc. (617) 263-2298	P.O.Box 592 Acton, MA 01720	M: steel and brass test blocks for Rockwell testers, diamond penetrators for all types of testers (cones, Vickers, and Knoop)
PSI Metallurgical Systems Co. (713) 467-9187	9610 Long Point Suite 107 Houston, TX 77055	D: testers (Rockwell, Brinell, Microhardness, Knoop, Vickers, portable, Scleroscopes, and Durometers)

[a] M = manufacture, D = distribute, S = service

Company/Phone No.	Address	Comments[a]
Quality Assurance Corp. (317) 353-6562	P.O. Box 19343 Indianapolis, IN 46219	D, S: testers (Rockwell, Brinell, Microhardness, Knoop, Vickers, portable, Durometers, automatic hardness testing systems); manufactures test blocks
Rams Rockford Products, Inc. (815) 964-9547	1517 Fulton Ave. Rockford, IL 61103	M, D, S: testers (Rockwell and portable); distributes accessories for all hardness testers, Rockwell and portable testers
Service Associated Inc. (312) 568-4545	339 W.112th Place Chicago, IL 60628	D, S: testers (Rockwell, Brinell, Microhardness, Knoop, Vickers, portable, Scleroscope, and Durometers); services Durometers
Service Physical Testers (313) 385-4436	6169 Lakeshore Rd Port Huron, MI 48060	M
Shore Instrument & Manufacturing Co. (516) 379-3400	80 Commercial St. Freeport, NY 11520	M, D, S: Scleroscopes and Durometers
Stangert Corp. (516) 432-4277	94 Long Beach Rd. Island Park, LI NY 11558	D, S: testers (Rockwell, Brinell, Microhardness, Knoop, Vickers, and portable)
Technicorp (201) 438-9005	153 Orchard St. E. Rutherford NJ 07073	M, D, S: thermoelectric testers that can distinguish annealled from hardened fusion metals
Technology & Calibration Inc. (713) 692-1600	4120 Siegel St. Houston, TX 77009	D, S: testers (Rockwell, Brinell, Microhardness, Knoop, Vickers and portable
Teleweld Inc. (815) 672-4561	416 N. Park St. Streator, IL 61364	M: Brinell and portable testers
Testing Equipment of American Inc. (203) 767-1649	48 Saybrook Road P.O. Box 466 Essex, CT 06426	M, D, S: Rockwell testers and Durometers
Testing Machines Inc. (516) 842-5400	400 Bayview Ave. Amityville, NY 11701	D, S: testers (Rockwell, Brinell Microhardness, and Durometers)
Timberline West Inc. (303) 945-7572	P.O. Box 1210 Glenwood Springs, CO 81602	M, D, S: portable Brinell testers

[a] M = manufacture, D = distribute, S = service

Company/Phone No.	Address	Comments[a]
Tinius Olsen Testing Machine Co. Inc. (215) 675-7100	P.O. Box 429 Willow Grove, PA 19090-0429	M, D, S: testers (Brinell and Rockwell); services Rockwell testers
United Calibration Corp. (714) 638-2322	12761 Monarch St. Garden Grove, CA 92641	M
United Service Co. CT (203) 667-4403 NE (800) 437-3013	P.O. Box 11136 Newington, CT 06111	D, S: testers (Rockwell, Brinell, Microhardness, Knoop, Vickers, portable, Scleroscopes, and Durometers); distributes test blocks and penetrators
United Testing Systems Inc. United Calibration Corp. (313) 852-7744	2165 Avon Industrial Dr. Auburn Heights MI 48057	M, D, S: testers (Rockwell, Brinell, Microhardness, Knoop, Vickers, portable, and Durometers); manufactures Rockwell and portable testers
United Testing Systems Inc. United Calibration Corp (714) 895-6396	5802 Engineer Dr. Huntington Beach CA 92649	M, D, S: testers (Rockwell, Brinell, Microhardness, Knoop, Vickers, portable, Scleroscopes and Durometers); manufactures test blocks and penetrators
Vickers Instruments Inc.	800 W. Cummings Pk. Suite 1900 Woburn, MA 01810	M, D: manufactures testers (Rockwell and Vickers); distributes Vickers testers
VWR Scientific Co. Inc. Div. of Univar (312) 547-3900	P.O. Box 66929 O'Hare AMF Chiago, IL 60666	D: testers (Brinell and Durometers
Walker Scientific Inc. (617) 852-3674	Rockdale St. Worcester, MA 01606	M
Washington Chain & Supply Inc. Div. of Engineering (206) 623-8500	2901 Utah Ave. S. Seattle, WA 98124	S: testers (Rockwell and Brinell)
Webster Instrument Inc. (213) 479-6770	11856 Mississippi Ave Los Angeles, CA 90025	M, D, S: portable testers
Carl Zeiss Inc. (914) 747-1800	One Zeiss Dr. Thornwood, NY 10594	M, D, S: Microhardness testers
Zwick of America Inc. (203) 623-9475	P.O. Box 997 18 Thompson Rd. E. Windsor, CT 06088	M, D, S: testers (Rockwell, Microhardness, Knoop, Vickers, and Durometers)

[a] M = manufacture, D = distribute, S = service

Appendix 4 Directory of Equipment Manufacturers and Suppliers in Canada

Company/Phone No.	Address	Comments[a]
Acco Measurement Systems of Canada (416) 675-3820	234 Attwell Drive Rexdale ON M9W 5B3	D, S: testers (Rockwell, Brinell Microhardness, Knoop, Vickers, and portable)
Anglo Canadian Scientific Co. Ltd. (416) 291-3336	85 Nugget Ave. Agincourt ON M1S 3B1	D, S: testers (Rockwell, Brinell, Microhardness, Knoop, Vickers, and portable)
Calibration Canada Ltd. (416) 689-8783	31 Dundee St. E. Hamilton ON L9J 1B1	D
Canadian N.D.E. Technology Ltd. (416) 243-3456	18 Canso Rd. Rexdale ON M9W 4L8	M, D
John Herring & Co. Ltd. (416) 727-1345	49 Yonge St. S. Aurora ON L4G 1L8	D: testers (Durometers and Barcol)
Hoskin Scientific Ltd. (416) 842-0237	1156 Speers Rd. Oakville ON L6L 2X4	D
JKS-Boyles International Inc. (416) 789-0611	81 Tycos Dr. Toronto ON M6B 1W5	D
Intertechnology Inc. (416) 445-5500	1 Scarsdale Rd. Don Mills ON M3B 2R2	D
L-K Industrial Instr. Service Ltd. (416) 459-2062	80 Hale Rd. Unit 10 Brampton ON L6W 2R2	M, D

[a] M = manufacture, D = distribute, S = service

Company/Phone No.	Address	Comments[a]
Leco Instruments Ltd. (416) 624-6933	5151 Everest Dr. Mississauga ON L4W 2R2	D, S: testers (Rockwell, Brinell, Microhardness, Knoop, Vickers, light-load Microhardness, automated hardness testers with programmable X-Y stages)
M & L Testing Equip. Co. (416) 689-7327	31 Dundee St. E. Highway 5 Hamilton ON L9J 1B1	M, D
Micro Metallurgical Ltd. (416) 889-6231	41 Maple Ave. Richmond Hill ON L4C 6P4	D, S: testers (Rockwell, Brinell, Microhardness, Knoop, Vickers, and portable)
Park Thermal Ltd. (416) 877-5254	62 Todd Rd. Georgetown ON L7G 4R7	M
Russell Ultra-Sound Services (NDT) Ltd. (403) 469-4461	4909 75th Ave. Edmonton AB T6B 2S3	M, D
Swiss Instruments Ltd. (416) 279-1275	1920 Mattawa Ave. Mississauga ON L4X 1K1	D: testers (Rockwell, Brinell, Microhardness, Knoop, Vickers, portable, and Durometers)
Tech-Met Canada Ltd/Ltee (416) 291-9831	80 Milner Ave. Unit 9 Scarborough ON M1S 3P8	D, S: testers (Rockwell, Brinell, Microhardness, Knoop, Vickers, portable, and Durometers)
United Testing Systems Canada Ltd. (416) 669-5327	225 Bradwick Drive Unit 21 Concord ON L4K 1K7	D, S: testers (Rockwell, Brinell, Microhardness, Knoop, Vickers, and portable)

[a] M = manufacture, D = distribute, S = service

INDEX

A

15N scale (Rockwell), applications, 53
15T scale (Rockwell), applications, 127, 143
30T scale (Rockwell), applications, 127, 143
Abrasion tests, 2, 12-15
Abrasives, 1-2, 13-14
Abrasive-wear tests, 12-14
Accuracy
    Brinell testing, 21-22
    file testing, 109
    Rockwell scale, 47
    Scleroscope testing, 96
    Vickers testing, 58-59
Alpha scale, Rockwell hardness testing, 128-129
Aluminum
    hardness testing, 124-126
    Rockwell scale for, 46, 125
Aluminum alloys
    Brinell test load for, 17
    B scale for, 46, 125
    hardness testing, 124-126
Aluminum-magnesium alloys, Rockwell scale for, 46, 125
Annealed alloys
    brass strip, minimum thickness, Scleroscope testing, 94
    Brinell testing, 20, 29
    hardness range, 142
    minimum thickness, Scleroscope testing, 94

Rockwell scale for, 46, 125
Anvil
    adapters, 36-39
    Brinell testing machine, 22-24
    effect, 49, 125
    for Rockwell testing, 44-45, 36-39
    Rockwell testing machine, schematic, 35
Anvil effect, 49, 125
Apatite, Mohs scale rating, 107
Apparent hardness, P/M parts, 118
Applications, hardness testing, 115-140
Area (of indentations)
    in Brinell testing, 11, 17
    and diameters, indentations, 104
    as hardness measure, 1, 11
    instant measurement, 102
    load to, 1
    as microhardness measure, 12
    ultrasonic microhardness testing, 98
    in Vickers testing, 59
    width, and spacing, effects of, 49
Argon atmosphere, elevated temperature Rockwell testing, 54-55
Armco iron, Mohs hardness, 107
A scale (Rockwell)
    applications, 46, 125
    for cemented carbides, 50, 123
    with diamond indenters, 47
    for low hardness values, 49
    for nonferrous metals, 124
    for titanium, 126

Atmospheres, heat treating, controlling, 87-88
Austenite. See Retained austenite.
Automatic Brinell hardness testing system, 22, 25
Automatic microhardness testers, applications, 72
Automatic Rockwell testing machines, 43-44

B

Ball bearings, eddy current testing, 113
Ball indenters. See also Balls.
  Brinell testing, 21
  B scale with, 49
  maximum readings for, 50
  minimum thickness table, 48
  portable Rockwell tester, 42
  Rockwell hardness by, 33-34
Balls. See also Ball indenters.
  carbide and steel, compared, 21
  cemented tungsten, 20
  hardened steel, 17
  hulked, Brinell testing, 21
  small diameter, Vickers testing, 64
  in static indentation tests, 1
  tungsten carbide, 17, 21
Base SI units, 158
Bearing metals, Rockwell scale for, 46, 125
Beryllium copper, Rockwell scale for, 46, 125
Bierbaum test, as plowing/scratch test, 2, 4
Black box, ultrasonic microhardness tester, 100
Bonded layers, microhardness measurement, 68
Brass
  hardness scale for, 120
  strip, minimum thickness, Scleroscope testing, 94
Brinell hammer, as comparator, 16
Brinell hardness number (HB)
  calculated, 17-18
  steel, approximate equivalent hardness numbers, 153
  as stress value, 23
  table, 19
Brinell indentations, process and types, 19-20
Brinell testing, 17-29. See also Brinell testing machines; Brinell tests.

applications, 29
  of cast irons, 115-116
  for high-production testing, 147
  indentation mark effects, 146
  of irons, 143
  limitations, 28-29
  machines for, 22-28
  measuring indentation, 11, 18-22
  of nonferrous metals, 124
  precautions, 28-29
  and Rockwell testing, compared, 31
  of specific materials, 29
Brinell testing machines. See also Brinell testing.
  automatic system, 22, 25
  hydraulic manually operated, 22, 23
  portable, 24-27
  semi-automatic air-operated, 22, 24
Brinell tests. See also Brinell testing.
  defined, 17
  deformed grid pattern in, 7
  hardness range, 29
  history, 4-5
  indentation process, 18
  loads for, 17
  as static indentation tests, 2
Brittleness, as hardness property, 1
Bronze, hardness scale for, 120
B scale (Rockwell)
  aluminum/aluminum alloys, 124
  applications, 46, 125
  with ball indenter, 49
  P/M parts, 121
Bulging, in microhardness testing, 81

C

Calcite, Mohs hardness, 107
Calibration
  of Brinell machines, 26-27
  elastic, 27
  and limits of error, 26-27
  micrometer microscope, Vickers testing, 59
  one-point, ultrasonic microhardness testing, 104
  optical system, microhardness tester, 73
  proving ring, 27
  of Rockwell testers, 51-55
  for testing P/M parts, 122

Canada, hardness testing equipment manufacturers, 171-172
Carbonitrided cases, microhardness testing, 83
Carburization
effect in Brinell testing, 22
monitoring, by microhardness testing, 68
and test selection, 145
Carburized case, Rockwell scales for, 47
Case, 121. See also Case depth; Effective case depth; Nitrided cases.
Case depth
deep, Rockwell scale for, 46, 125
and depth of indentation, 136
hardness testing, 134-138
measurement methods, 137
medium, Rockwell scale for, 46, 125
by microhardness testing, 68, 82-83, 86-87
shallow, Rockwell scale for, 46, 125
Case hardened steels
Brinell testing, 29
case depth hardness testing, 134-138
hardness traverses, 105-106
Rockwell testing, 46, 53, 125
Scleroscope testing, 94
Cast alloys, hardness range, 142-143
Cast irons
Brinell testing, 17, 29
hard, C scale for, 46, 125
hardness range, 143
hardness testing, 115-118
Rockwell scale for, 46, 125
small, 116
test selection for, 146
true hardness by microhardness testing, 143
Cast nonferrous metals, test selection for, 146
Cast steels, test selection for, 146
Cemented carbides
A scale for, 50
Brinell testing, 29
hardness testing, 122-123
Rockwell scale for, 46, 125
Cemented tungsten, balls, 20
Chromium-vanadium carbide, microhardness of, 85
Circular workpieces, Brinell testing, 25
Class 30 gray iron, testing composite, 116

Classification, of hardness tests, 1-2, 15-16
Cobalt binder, hardness measurement, 123
Cold finished steel strip, minimum thickness, Scleroscope testing, 94
Cold worked alloys, Brinell indentations in, 20
Cold working
effect, indentation spacing, 49
effect, Scleroscope testing, 94
Compact, iron-graphite sintered, microstructure, 119
Comparators, in high-production testing, 15-16
Composites, hardness testing, 122-123
Cone
diamond, as Rockwell indenter, 31-32
static indentation tests with, 1
Constant maximum shear stress, Hertz lines, 7-8
Constraint factor, defined, 5
Contact pressure, in laboratory wear tests, 13
Conversion
charts, durometer-plastometer, 135
factors, SI units, 160-162
and metric data, 157-162
tables, interpreting, 86
Copper, hardness testing, 107, 126
Copper alloys
Brinell test load for, 17
B scale for, 46, 125
hardness testing, 126
Core
hardness traverse, 136
microhardness testing, 83
Correction factors
for cylindrical workpieces, Rockwell testing, 50-51
table, for cylindrical workpieces, 51
for workpiece shape, 144
Corundum, Mohs scale rating, 107
Counterweighted anvil adapters, Rockwell testing, 36, 37
Crankshafts. See also Shafts.
Scleroscope testing, 93, 96
ultrasonic microhardness testing, 100-101
C scale (Rockwell)
applications, 46, 125
calibration, 52
with diamond indenters, 47

Cure, hardness tests as indicating, 128
Cutting
  resistance to, 1
  tests, defined, 2
Cyaniding, file testing of, 109
Cylindrical workpieces, 39, 50-52, 132

D

Damping, elastic, 1
Damping tests, defined, 2
Decarburization
  detected by file testing, 108
  detected by microhardness testing, 68, 87-88
  detected by Rockwell testing, 53
  detected by Scleroscope testing, 96
  detected by ultrasonic microhardness testing, 101
  surface, effect in Brinell testing, 22
  and test selection, 145
Deformation
  of Brinell indenters, 27-28
  permanent, 1
Depth. See also Depth of indentation.
  of indentation, as hardness measure, 11
  penetration, 22-23, 25, 31, 47
  vs thickness, copper/copper alloys, 126
Depth of indentation. See also Indentations; Penetration depth; Spacing of indentations.
  Brinell, calculated, 28-29
  and case depth, 136
  as hardness measure, 11
  and minimum indentation thickness, 98
  Rockwell, computing, 47
  ultrasonic microhardness testing, 97
  Vickers testing, 57, 57-58
Depth of penetration. See Penetration depth.
Derived SI units, 158-159
Dial gages
  automatic, 43-44
  correction factors for, 50
  Model D Scleroscope, 92
  Rockwell testing machine, 35
Diamond

  cone, as Rockwell indenter, 31-32
  Mohs scale rating, 107
  and titanium, affinity effect, 126-127
Diamond indenters. See also Indenters.
  Brale, minimum thickness table, 48
  for case hardened steel, 53
  for cemented carbides, 123
  cone, Rockwell testing, 31-33, 42
  maximum hardness, 50
  for microhardness testing, 67
  minimum readings for, 49-50
  for nonferrous metals, 124
  portable Rockwell machines, 42
  pyramid, elastic recovery distortions, 103
  pyramid, types, for microhardness testing, 68
  pyramid, for Vickers testing, 57-58
  Rockwell scales with, 47
  for Vickers testing, 57-58
Diamond Pyramid hardness, 21, 59-62, 154-155
Diamond pyramid hardness test. See Vickers hardness tests.
Diamond pyramid indenters. See Diamond indenters; Indenters.
Diamond-tipped hammer, in Scleroscopes, 89
Die blocks, Scleroscope testing, 93
Digital readout
  Brinell hardness numbers, 22, 25
  correction factors for, 50
  durometers with, 134
  Model D Scleroscope tester, 93
  Rockwell testers, 44, 45
  Scleroscope, 93
Directory, equipment manufacturers/suppliers, 163-172
Direct reading machines, Brinell, 23
Dry-sand abrasion test, 14-15
D scale (Rockwell)
  applications, 46, 125
  with diamond indenters, 47
  for low hardness values, 49
Ductile irons
  and gray irons, observed/ converted hardness, 119
  hardness range, 143
  hardness testing, 116, 118
Durometers, 130-135

E

Eddy current testing
applications, 110
for checking ball bearings, 113
electromagnetic testing, 110-113
limitations, 112-113
principle, 109
tester, 111-113
Edge angle, Vickers testing, 57-58
Edges (of workpiece)
in Brinell testing, 21
hardness traverse for, 136
microhardness measurement, 68
readings, ultrasonic
microhardness testing, 106
Effective case depth. See also Case
depth.
defined, 136
microhardness testing, 121
standard, case hardened
workpieces, 53
thickness, for Rockwell testing,
47-48
Elastic calibration, for Brinell
testers, 27
Elastic-constraint factor, defined,
9
Elastic damping, and hardness, 1
Elastic deflection, calculated, 27
Elasticity
high modules of, 1
in plastics, 128
in slip-line-field theory, 7
Elastic-plastic flow boundary, 7-8
Elastic recovery
distortion, ultrasonic
microhardness testing, 103
in microhardness testing, 80-81,
103
in plastics, 128
Elastic theory of hardness, 5-10
Electromagnetic testing, 110-113
applications, 111-112
defined, 2
equipment for, 110-111
harmonic comparator, 111
methods, 14-15
principle, 110
Elevated temperatures, Rockwell
testing at, 54-55
Elevating screw, Rockwell tester,
45, 51
End-quench curve, developing,
139-140
End-quench test, 138-140
Equipment. See also Machines.
for electromagnetic testing,
110-111

manufacturers, Canada, 171-172
manufacturers, United States,
163-169
optical, microhardness testers, 72
for Vickers testing, 58-65
Erosion tests, 2, 12-13
Error(s). See also Limits of error.
in Brinell testing, 28-29
limits, Brinell testing, 26-27
sources, microhardness testing,
71, 79-81
tester, 26-27
with ultrasonic microhardness
testing, 102
Vickers testing, 59
E scale (Rockwell)
for aluminum hardness, 125
applications, 46, 125
for magnesium/magnesium alloys,
126
for zinc sheet, 127
Eyepiece, filar, 4, 65, 72-75

F

Failure analysis, microhardness
testing for, 85-86
Feldspar, Mohs scale rating, 107
Ferrous metals, Brinell load
application, 17
Filar eyepiece, 4, 65, 72-75
Filar units, eyepiece, microhardness
testing, 74-75
File hard, defined, 108
File testing, 107-109
for decarburization, 108
methods, 12
as scratch test, 2
Filing, for Scleroscope testing, 94
Fillet radii, ultrasonic microhardness
testing, 100-101
Fine pearlite, hardness
measurement, 121
Finishing. See also Surface
conditions; Surface(s).
for Scleroscope testing, 94
Fixtures
for microhardness testers, 73-74
ultrasonic microhardness tester,
100
Flat-ended punch, in slip-line-field
theory, 5-9
Flat-type Brinell impression,
18, 20
Flat workpieces

and hardness test selection,
144-145
piling of, 49
ultrasonic microhardness testing,
100-101
Flow
constraint, defined, 6
Hill's pattern, 5-8
patterns, slip-line-field theory,
5-11
Prandtl's pattern, 5-8
stress, 1, 5
Fluorite, Mohs scale rating, 107
Flux density, in electromagnetic
testing, 2
Foil, microhardness testing, 68, 82
Free graphite, and hardness testing,
115
Friction, 10-11, 58
F scale (Rockwell)
for aluminum hardness, 125
applications, 46, 125

G

Gears
portable Rockwell tester for, 42
tooth flanks, ultrasonic
microhardness testing, 102
worm, Brinell testing machine, 22
Glass tube, Scleroscope, 89, 90
Goose-neck anvil adapters,
Rockwell testing, 36-39
Graphite carbon, P/M parts, 118
Gray irons
and ductile irons, observed/
converted hardness, 119
hardness range, 143
hardness testing, 115-116
Grid pattern, from Brinell test, 7
Grinding
abrasion, high-stress, 14
for Scleroscope testing, 94
for ultrasonic microhardness
testing, 106
wheels, erosion hardness test for, 2
Grinding burn, 68, 96
G scale (Rockwell), applications, 46,
125
Gypsum, Mohs hardness, 107

H

Half-hard brass strip, minimum
thickness, Scleroscope testing, 94

Hammer, diamond-tipped, 89-93
Hardenability, hardness testing
evaluation, 138
Hardened steels. See also Case
hardened steels; Steels.
balls, Brinell testing, 17
Brinell testing, 21, 29
minimum thickness, Scleroscope
tests, 94
Hard metals, Brinell hardness range,
29
Hardness
apparent, 118
Brinell, calculated, 17-18
converted and observed, cast
irons, 119
defined, 1, 3, 11
indentation tests, compared, 98
indirect measurement, 109
and load combinations, for
minimum thickness, micro-
hardness testing, 82
measurement, Brinell, limits, 21
properties, 1
range, 29, 142
as resistance to plastic flow, 3
surveys, 71
true, 11, 118
Hardness conversion tables
introduction, 149
for steel, 150-155
Hardness numbers
approximate equivalent, Brinell
hardness numbers for steel, 153
approximate equivalent, for
Rockwell B/C hardness
numbers, 151-152
vs load, microhardness number,
79-81
in microhardness testing, 74-78
for ultrasonic microhardness
testing, 98
Hardness profile curves, ultrasonic
microhardness testing, 104
Hardness range, for hardness test
selection, 142-143
Hardness survey, 71, 83-84
Hardness testing. See also Hardness
testing applications.
abrasion tests, 2
applications, 115-140
approaches to, 1-3
Brinell, 17-29
classes of, 15-16
common concepts of, 3-4
cutting tests, 2
damping tests, 2

eddy current, 109-113
electromagnetic testing, 2
erosion tests, 2
file, 107-109
history, 4-11
indentation, types compared, 98
introduction, 1-16
Knoop microhardness, 67-70
macrohardness, defined, 3-4
methods of, 11-15, 141-147
microhardness, 3-4, 67-88
on-site, 101, 105, 143-144
plastics, 127-134
plowing tests, 2
purpose, 3
rebound tests, 2
Rockwell, 31-55
Scleroscope, 89-97
scratch, 2, 107-109
static indentation tests, 1-2
test selection, 141-147
test types, 1-2
theory of, 5-11
ultrasonic methods, 2, 97-107
ultrasonic microhardness, 97-107
Vickers, 57-65
Vickers microhardness, 67-70
Hardness testing applications,
115-140. See also Hardness testing.
case depth, 134-138
hardenability evaluation, 138
nonferrous metals, 124-127
nonhomogeneous materials,
115-123
nonmetallic materials, 127-134
test bars, end-quench test,
138-140
Hardness traverses, 105-106, 136
Hardness values, minimum work-
metal, Rockwell hardness testers,
48
Harmonic comparator, electromagnetic testing, 111
Heat-checking, ultrasonic
microhardness testing for, 101
Heat-treated hardness scale, P/M
parts, 120
Herbert pendulum test, as damping
test, 2
Hertz lines, constant maximum
shear stress, 8
High-production testing. See also
Production testing.
defined, 16
High-speed eddy-current tester,
ball bearing
hardness, 113

High-stress grinding abrasion, 14
Hill's flow pattern, 5-6
History, of hardness testing, 4-11
Homogeneous materials
Brinell testing, 29
nonferrous, 124
Hopper, vibratory, Rockwell testers,
44
H scale (Rockwell)
for aluminum hardness, 125
applications, 46, 125
for zinc sheet, 127
Hulked ball, Brinell testing, 21
Hydraulic Brinell testing machine,
22, 23
Hydraulic portable Brinell
hardness tester, 26

I

Impact
effect, microhardness testing, 71
resiliency, defined, 12
sound, in Scleroscope testing, 95
Impressions, ridging- and sinking-
type, Brinell, 19-20
Indentation depth. See Depth of
indentation.
Indentation hardness tests,
compared, 98
Indentations. See also Depth of
indentation; Indentation testing;
Penetration depth; Spacing of
indentations.
area of, 12
Brinell, 18, 20, 21, 28
corners, in Vickers testing, 59
depth, as hardness measure, 11
diameter, spacing by, 49
diamond pyramid, distortion in,
103-104
elastic recovery in, 81, 103-104
with equal diameters, differing
areas, 104
flat, Brinell, 18, 20
Knoop, microconstituents
compared, 85
marks, effects, 146-147
measuring, microhardness testing,
74
multiple, testing, 86-88
network pattern, 71
optimum size, 78
oval, 144
process, Brinell, 18

pyramidal Knoop indenter with, 69
rhombic-shaped, microhardness, 68-69
ridging-type Brinell, 20
round, 17-18
shape, Knoop and Vickers, compared, 69-70
sinking-type Brinell, 19-20
size, in microhardness testing, 67
slip-line-field solution for two-dimensional, 10
ultrasonic microhardness testing, 97
Vickers, 58
Indentation spacing. See Spacing of indentations.
Indentation testing. See also Indentations; Static indentation tests.
dynamic, Scleroscope hardness as, 12
reversing principle of, 11-12
Indenters. See also Diamond indenters; Knoop indenters.
ball, 21
blunt, and elastic theory of hardness, 10
Brinell testing, 21
carbide, 55
common, 5
deformation, 27-28
for durometers, 130
effect on cylindrical workpieces, 51
for elevated temperature testing, 55
with frames, 37, 40
Knoop and Vickers, compared, 69
Knoop microhardness, 68-70
microhardness tester, 72
minimum thickness table, 48
for plastics, 128
for porous workpieces, microhardness testing, 121
retractable, in steel shroud, 38
rhombic-base pyramidal, 68-69
Rockwell, 31-32
Rockwell, schematic, 35
sapphire, 55
spring-loaded, 131-134
steel ball, minor/major loads, 32
for steels, 143
Tukon hardness tester, 108
Vickers, 57-58
Vickers microhardness, 68-70
Indexing, in Rockwell testing system, 54-55
Interpretation of results

Brinell testing, 20
case depth measurement, 135
microhardness testing, 86
Rockwell testing, 44
Scleroscope testing, 95-96, 97
In-tolerance limits, Rockwell testing, 44
Iron-carbon P/M parts, hardness scales for, 120
Iron-graphite compact, sintered, microstructure, 119
Iron-nickel-carbon P/M parts, hardness scales, 120

J

Jigs
calibrated, for Vickers testing, 65
quenching, for jominy (end-quench) test, 139
Jominy (end-quench) test, 138-140

K

Knife-edge micrometer ocular, Vickers tester, 63-64
Knoop hardness number (KHN or HK)
defined, 69
determining, 75, 78
for load of 1 gf, 75-78
Knoop indenters
for microhardness testing, 68-70
for porous materials, 121
and Vickers indenter, compared, 69
Knoop microhardness testing
development, 67
indenters and indentations, and Vickers, compared, 69-70
principle, 67
as static indentation test, 2
tester, load and hardness combinations, 82
K scale (Rockwell), applications, 46, 125

L

Laboratory hardness testing
microhardness, 68
process control, 16
types, 15-16

wear tests, 13-14
Lead, Rockwell scale for, 46, 125
Lighting, for microhardness testers, 72
Limits of error, 26-27. See also Error(s).
Linear variable differential transducer, Scleroscope tester, 93
Load. See also Load application; Major load; Minor load.
  to area, as hardness measure, 1
  for Brinell test, hard metals, 17
  for Brinell test, nonferrous alloys, 29
  for Brinell test, soft metals, 17
  deadweight, microhardness tester, 71
  dependence, microhardness testing, 80-81
  direction, Brinell testing, 28
  gage, Brinell testing machine, 22
  Knoop and Vickers tests, compared, 69-70
  major, Rockwell test, 31-33
  microhardness testing, 67, 71, 78-82, 97
  minor, Rockwell test, 31-33
  range, in microhardness testers, 71
  selection, microhardness testing, 78
  single, 104
  ultrasonic microhardness testing, 97
  uniform, Brinell tests, 22
  Vickers testing, 58
Load application. See also Load.
  in Brinell testing, 22, 26, 28
  in portable Brinell testers, 26
  rate, effect, microhardness testing, 71
  Rockwell testing, 45
  Vickers testing, 58, 64
Load gage, Brinell testing machine, 22
Load range, microhardness testers, 71-72
Low-frequency comparator-bridge-type instruments, 15
Low-stress scratching abrasion, 14, 15
L scale (Rockwell), applications, 46, 125

M

Machines. See also Equipment.

for Brinell testing, 22-28
  harmonic comparator, 111
  portable, 24-26
  for production testing, 22-24
  for Rockwell testing, 35-44
Machining, for Scleroscope testing, 94
Macrohardness testing, 3-4
Magnesium alloys, hardness testing, 46, 125-126
Magnesium, hardness testing, 126
Magnetism, as hardness property, 1
Main spring, durometers, 130
Maintenance, hardness testers, 27-28, 51-55
Major load. See also Load; Minor load.
  plastics, 127
  Rockwell test, defined, 31-33, 45
  superficial Rockwell testing, 33
Malleability, as hardness property, 1
Malleable irons
  B scale for, 46, 125
  cast, hardness conversions, 117
  hardness range, 143
  hardness testing, 115
  pearlitic, C scale for, 46, 125
Manufacturers, equipment, 163-172
Martensite needles, hardness measurement, 121
Mass-production hardness testing, test selection, 147
Matrix hardness, tests for, 116
Maximum-shear theory, 7-8
Melting temperatures, high, as hardness property, 1
Metallographic emery papers, 106
Metric and conversion data, 157-162
Microconstituents, hardness measurement, 68, 84-85
Microhardness, defined, 67
Microhardness testers. See also Microhardness testing.
  automatic, 72
  components, 72
  fixtures for, 73-74
  optical equipment, 72-73
  types, 71-81
Microhardness testing, 67-88
  applications, 68, 81-88
  cemented carbides, 123
  defined, 3-4, 12
  to detect decarburization, 53, 68, 87-88
  to detect retained austenite, 87
  to estimate case depth, 68, 86-87

for failure analysis, 85-86
for flat workpieces, 144-145
hardness number determination, 74-78
hardness number vs load, 79-81
indentation mark effects, 146
Knoop, 67-70
measuring indentation, 74
for microconstituent hardness, 84
for monitoring surface-hardening processes, 82-84
parts tested, 3-4
in process control laboratories, 16
of porous materials, 121
for quality control, 123
sequence for, 79
for shop problems, 84-85
of small workpieces, 81-82
spacing of indentations, 79
specimen preparation/handling, 73-74
testers, 71-81
ultrasonic, 97-107
Vickers, 67-70
with Vickers indenter, conversion table, 59-62
for workpiece edge measurement, 68

Micrometer
microscope, in Vickers testing, 59
ocular, knife-edge, Vickers tester, 63-64
screw, microhardness tester, 71-72

Microscope, Vickers tester, 63

Microstructure
averaging, by load size, 122
sintered iron-graphite compact, 119

Minerals, Mohs hardness of, 107-108

Minimum thickness tables,
Rockwell testing, 48

Minor load. See also Load; Load application; Major load.
Rockwell test, defined, 31-33, 45
superficial Rockwell testing, 33

Mobile Rockwell hardness testers, 41-42

Model C-2 Scleroscope, 90, 94-97

Model C-3 Scleroscope, 91, 94-97

Model D Scleroscope, 91-92, 94-97

Model D Scleroscope dial, 92

Modulus of elasticity, 1, 98

Mohs hardness scale, 2, 4, 107

Monitoring, of surface-hardening processes, 82-84

Monotron tester, as indentation testing, 11-12

Motorized Rockwell production testing machine, 43

Mounting
durometers, 132
microhardness testers, 73
Scleroscopes, 92

M scale (Rockwell), applications, 46, 125

Multiple-indentation testing, 87-88

N

Nitrided cases
file testing, 109
microhardness testing, 68, 83
Rockwell scale for, 47
true hardness of, 11

Nondestructive tests
electromagnetic, 110-113
ultrasonic microhardness testing, 97

Nonferrous metals
aluminum/aluminum alloys, 124-126
Brinell and Rockwell testing, 124
Brinell testing, 29, 124
copper/copper alloys, 126
hardness range, 142
magnesium/magnesium alloys, 126
titanium, 126-127
zinc, 127

Nonhomogeneous materials
Brinell testing, 29
cast irons, 115-118
cemented carbides, 122-123
hardness testing, 115-123
P/M parts, 118-122

N scale (Rockwell), superficial hardness tester, 46n, 125n

O

Objectives, types for microhardness testing, 73

On-site hardness testing
types, 143-144
ultrasonic microhardness, 101, 105

Optical equipment, microhardness testers, 72-73

O rings, durometer testing, 131

Orthoclase (feldspar), Mohs scale rating, 107

Oscilloscope, electromagnetic
  readout by, 111-112
Outboard anvil adapters, Rockwell
  testing machines, 36, 37
Overheating, hardness
  testing effects, 86, 94
Overloading, effect, Brinell testing,
  22, 28

P

Particle size, of abrasives, 13
Parts. See also P/M parts.
  case hardened, Rockwell testing,
    53
  for macrohardness testing, 3
  for microhardness testing, 3-4
  for Rockwell testers, 36, 53
Pearlitic malleable irons, hardness
  testing, 46, 116, 125
Pencil-type durometer, 133
Pendulum test, Herbert, 2
Penetration depth. See also Depth
of indentation; Indentations.
  readout, Brinell testing, 22-23, 25
  Rockwell testing, 31, 47
Penetration resistance, as
  hardness property, 1
Penetrators. See Indenters.
Permanent deformation, in
  hardness evaluation, 11
Phosphor bronze, Rockwell scale
  for, 46, 125
Plastic deformation, resistance to, 1
Plastic flow
  and hardness, 1, 3, 11
  in slip-line-field theory, 5-11
  stress, 1
Plasticity, in slip-line-field theory, 7
Plastic recovery, defined, 10
Plastic-rigid theory, 5-9
Plastics
  alpha scale use, 129
  durometer specifications, 130
  durometer testing, 131-134
  hardness testing, 127-134
  testing procedure, 127-128
Plastomer-durometer conversion
  chart, 135
Plates, Rockwell tester for, 41
Plating, microhardness
  measurement, 68
PL model Rockwell testers, 128
Plowing tests, defined, 2
P/M parts. See also Parts.

apparent hardness and
  microhardness of, 118
  Brinell testing, 29
  hardness testing, 118-122
  material, effect on test selection,
    145-146
  Rockwell hardness scales for, 120
Polarized light, for microhardness
  testing, 73
Polishing
  for microhardness testing, 73
  Scleroscope workpieces, 94
  ultrasonic microhardness testing,
    106
Porosity
  effect, hardness testing, 115, 120
  effect, microhardness, 121
  effect, P/M parts, 118-122
  of wrought material, 121-122
Portability, testing machine, and
  workpiece size, 143
Portable hardness testers
  Brinell, 24-26
  principle of, 42
  Rockwell, 41-42
  Scleroscope, 96
  ultrasonic microhardness, 104-105
Powder metallurgy parts. See P/M
  parts.
Prandtl's flow pattern, 5-6
Prealloyed steel, hardness scales for,
  120
Precipitation-hardenable alloys,
  hardness testing, 126
Pressure gage, Brinell testing
  machines, 22
Primary coil, eddy current testing,
  109
Probes
  eddy current testing, 109
  ultrasonic microhardness tester,
    100
Process control laboratories,
  hardness testing, 16, 68
Production testing
  Brinell machines for, 22-24
  high, automatic Rockwell testing
    system, 43
  high, defined, 16
  Rockwell hardness, 43-44
  semi-automatic air-operated
    Brinell tester, 24
  test selection for, 147
Proving rings, Brinell testing, 22, 27
P scale (Rockwell), applications, 46,
  125

Pump, hydraulic, Brinell testing machine, 22
Punches, types, 5-7
Punching quality, laminated sheet, hardness testing for, 128
Pyramidal Knoop indenter, with indentation, 69

Q

Quadrant-style durometers, 131-132
Quality control
cemented carbides, microhardness testing, 123
laboratory, 16
microhardness testing for, 81
Quartz, Mohs scale rating, 107
Quenching jig, for jominy end-quench test, 139

R

Readings
Brinell tests, 22, 25
for calibration, 52
digital readout, Brinell hardness numbers, 22, 25
electromagnetic testing, 111
end-quench test, 139-140
glass, Sceroscope tester, 96
hardness survey, microhardness tester, 83
microhardness, 74-75, 83
for porous materials, 120
Rockwell testing, 33, 50
Sceroscope testing, 95-96, 95, 97
Shore hardness scale, 93
Spencer Bierbaum instrument, 4
ultrasonic, in-shop, 106
Vickers testers, 59, 63-64
Rebound
principle, usage, 12
scale, 89
tests, 2, 3, 89
Reference bars, Sceroscope testers, 96
Reproducibility
of end-quench test, 138
Rockwell scale, 47
Residual compressible stresses, and hardness testing theory, 10
Resistance

to low-stress scratching abrasion, 15
types, as hardness factors, 1
to wear, 12-13
Retained austenite
hardness measurement, 121
indentation hardness testing for, 53
microhardness testing of, 84, 87
and test selection, 145
Rhombic-base pyramidal indenters, microhardness, 68-69
Ridging, in Brinell testing, 19-20
Rockwell B hardness numbers, steel, approximate equivalent hardness numbers for, 151
Rockwell C hardness numbers, steel, approximate equivalent hardness numbers for, 152
Rockwell hardness testing, 31-55. See also Rockwell hardness testing machines; Rockwell hardness tests; Rockwell scales; Superficial Rockwell testing.
advantages, 31
and Brinell testing, compared, 31
of case hardened parts, 53
defined, 31, 33
for high-production testing, 147
indentation marks, effects, 147
machines for, 35-44
of nonferrous metals, 124
for P/M parts, 120
principle of, 31-35
procedure, 44-51
production testing, 43-44, 147
scale selection, 46-47
steels tested by, 143
superficial, defined, 34
surface conditions for, 145
types, 33-34
Rockwell hardness testing machines. See also Rockwell hardness testing.
calibration and maintenance, 51-55
components, 35, 36
customized, 38
for elevated temperatures, 54
modifications, 36-39
motorized, 43
PL models, 128
portable, 41-42
schematic, 35
and superficial Rockwell machines, combined, 35-36
top-loading, 38, 45

vertical workpiece supports, 37, 40
Rockwell hardness tests
  depth of indentation, 11, 47
  history, 5
  minimum work-metal hardness
    values, 48
  principle, schematic, 32
  procedure, 31-32
  scale designations, 34
  as static indentation test, 2
Rockwell scales
  designations, 34
  limitations of, 49-50
  for nonferrous metals, 124-127
  selection, 46-47
  types and applications, 46, 125
Round-type durometers, 131-132
R scale (Rockwell), applications, 46,
  125
Rubber rollers, hardness testing, 132
Rubbers, hardness testing, 131-134

S

Salt baths, microhardness testing,
  53, 87-88
Samples. See also Workpieces.
  representative, in hardness testing,
    15
Sand, for abrasion/erosion tests, 2,
  14-15
Sapphire indenters, for elevated
  temperature Rockwell testing, 55
Scales
  Bierbaum test, 4
  for case hardened steel parts, 53
  for P/M parts, 120
  rebound, 89
  Rockwell, 34, 45-50, 125
Scleroscope hardness testers. See
also Scleroscope hardness testing.
  advantages, 96-97
  history, 89
  Model C-2 Scleroscope, 90
  Model C-3 Scleroscope, 90, 91
  Model D Scleroscope, 90, 91-93
  rebound principle, 12
Scleroscope hardness testing,
  89-97
  advantages/limitations, 96-97
  applications, 96
  calibration, 96
  history, 89
  procedure, 94-97
  readings, 95-96

as rebound testing, 2
  and Rockwell C/Brinell hardness,
    89, 149-157
  testers, 90-94
  workpiece surface finish for, 94
  workpiece thickness, 94
Scratch hardness testing, 107-109
  defined, 2, 2, 4
  instruments, 107-108
  methods, 12
  Mohs scale of hardness, 107
  Tukon hardness tester with, 108
Sensitivity
  with diamond indenters, 49
  Rockwell scale, 47
  ultrasonic microhardness testing,
    104
Service life, wear rates for, 13-14
Setups
  automatic, microhardness tester,
    72
  eddy current testing, 112
  harmonic comparator, 111
  for Rockwell testing, cylindrical
    workpieces, 37, 39, 40-41, 44-45
  ultrasonic microhardness testing,
    100-101
Shadowgraph, for indenter
  inspection, 52
Shafts. See also Crankshafts.
  Rockwell testing, 36, 37
Shape (workpiece), 29, 144
Shear stress, constant maximum,
  708
Sheet metals
  minimum thickness for
    microhardness testing, 82
  Scleroscope testing, 94
  soft, Rockwell scale for, 46, 125
  thin, portable Rockwell tester for,
    42
  thin, scales for, 143
  ultrasonic microhardness testing
    fixtures, 100
  zinc, hardness testing, 127
Shield slip-line-field solution, 6
Shops, hardness testing in, 15, 84-85
Shore hardness scale, 93
Shot peening, and elastic theory of
  hardness, 10
Sinking, in Brinell testing, 19-20
Sintered cemented carbides,
  hardness testing, 122-123
Sintered hardness scale, P/M
  parts, 120
Sintered iron-graphite compact,
  microstructure, 119

Sintered steels, microhardness
testing, 121
SI prefixes, names and symbols, 160
SI units, base, supplementary,
derived, 158-159
Size
optimum, of indentations, 78
workpiece, Brinell testing, 29
workpiece, and hardness test
selection, 143-144
workpiece, nonferrous, 124
Slip-line-field solutions
flat-ended circular punch, 6
for flat-ended two-dimensional
punch, 5-6
for two-dimensional indentation,
10
Slip-line field theory, 5-11
and elastic theory, compared, 9
friction in, 10-11
Soft metals
Brinell hardness range, 29
B scale for, 46, 125
Rockwell scales for, 46, 125
Sorting
by electromagnetic testing, 15, 111
for high-production testing, 147
tolerance limit, Brinell testing, 23,
25
Spacing of indentations. See also
Indentations.
Brinell testing, 21, 21
and calibration, 52, 52
case depth measurement, 137
effects, in Rockwell testing, 49
microhardness testing, 79,
nonferrous metals, 124
Rockwell testing, 49, 49
Specimen preparation. See also
Workpieces.
microhardness testing, 73-74
**Spencer Bierbaum scratch-
hardness test,** 2, 4
Spring constant, determining, 129
S scale (Rockwell), applications,
46, 125
Stage, microscope, microhardness
testers, 71-72, 79
Standard test blocks, 51-52, 79, 96,
123
Static indentation tests
defined, 1-2
theory, 5-11
types and usage, 2-3
Steel ball indenters, Rockwell
testing, 31
Steels. See also Case hardened steels;

Hardened steels.
Brinell test load for, 17
C scale for, 46, 125
hardness conversion for, 150
prealloyed, hardness scales, 120
soft, B scale for, 46, 125
thin, Rockwell scale for, 46, 125
Steel shroud, for Rockwell
retractable indenter, 38
Step grinding technique, case
depth measurement, 137-138
Strain hardening, and elastic theory
of hardness, 10
Strength, high, as hardness property,
1
Stress
biaxial residual compressible, 10
residual compressible, 10
uniaxial, 5
value, Brinell hardness number as,
23
value, Knoop/Vickers hardness
values as, 78
Strip steel, Rockwell depth of
indentation, 47
**Superficial Rockwell hardness
testers,** for Vickers testing, 64
Superficial Rockwell testing. See
also Rockwell hardness testing.
correction values for cylindrical
workpieces, 51
defined, 34
hardness values, 34
major/minor loads, 33
minimum work-metal hardness
values, 48
portable, 42
principles, 34
scales for, 46, 125-126
T scales, for aluminum hardness,
126
Supplementary SI units, 158-159
Suppliers, hardness testing
equipment, 163-172
Surface area. See Area.
Surface conditions. See also Surface
preparation; Surface(s).
effect on Brinell testing, 21-22, 29
and hardness test selection, 145
for ultrasonic microhardness
testing, 106
Surface-hardening processes,
monitoring by microhardness
testing, 82-84
Surface preparation
for Brinell testing, 21-22

microhardness testing, porous
materials, 121
Surface roughness, Rockwell scale
for, 45
Surface(s)
for Brinell testing, 21-22
curved, 28
decarburization, microhardness
tested, 87-88
hardening processes, monitoring,
82-84
layers, microhardness
measurement, 68
for Rockwell testing, 45
for Scleroscope testing, 94
thin, file testing of, 109
Systeme International d'Unites
(SI), metric and conversion data,
157-162

T

Talc, Mohs hardness, 107
Tapered traverse, defined, 136-137
Tap tooth, microhardness tested,
85-86
Temperatures
elevated, Rockwell testing at,
54-55
high melting, as hardness
property, 1
measurement, electromagnetic, 14
Tempered alloys, Brinell testing, 29
Tensile strength, from conversion
tables, 86
Test bars, end-quench test, 138-140
Test blocks
A scale, 123
microhardness tester, 79
for Rockwell testers, 51-52
Scleroscope testing, 96
Testpieces. See Samples;
Workpieces.
Theory, of hardness testing, 5
Thermocouples, in elevated
temperature Rockwell testing, 55
Thickness
vs depth, copper/copper alloys,
126
minimum, for indentation tests, 98
minimum, for microhardness
testing, 82
nonferrous metals, 124
for Scleroscope testing, 94
of sheet, and hardness range, 143
workpiece, Brinell testing, 28

workpiece, Rockwell testing, 47-49
Thin
sheet, portable Rockwell tester for,
42
strip, Scleroscope testing, 94
Titanium, hardness testing, 46,
125-126
Tolerance limit sorting, Brinell
testing, 23, 25
Tool rooms, Scleroscope testing in,
96
Tool steels
hardened, Mohs hardness, 107
microhardness testing, 84-85, 88
Topaz, Mohs scale rating, 107
Top-loading Rockwell testers, 38,
45
Total case depth, defined, 1, 136
Traverses, hardness, 105-106, 136
True hardness. See also Hardness.
of cast irons, 143
cemented carbides, 123
of nitrided cases, 11-12
P/M parts, microconstituent
measurement for, 118, 146
as wear resistance, determining,
146
T scale (Rockwell)
aluminum hardness, 126
Rockwell testing, 46n, 125n
Tukon hardness tester, scratch test
with, 108
Tungsten carbide
balls, 17, 21
in cobalt matrix, 123
Tup, defined, 12

U

Ultrasonic hardness testers. See
also Ultrasonic microhardness testing.
applications, 100-102
components, 98-99
setups, specific testing, 100-102
testing of fillet radii by, 100-101
Ultrasonic microhardness testing,
97-107
capabilities, 102-105
defined, 2
limitations, 105-107
for nonflat workpieces, 145
portability, 105
setups, specific testing conditions,
100-101
surface finish requirements, 106
Uniaxial flow stress, as hardness
value, 5

United States, hardness testing
equipment manufacturers,
163-169

V

Vacuum furnace, for elevated
temperature Rockwell testing, 54
V-anvil, effect on testing cylindrical
workpieces, 51
Vibration, effects,
microhardness/Scleroscope testing,
71, 95
Vibratory hopper, Rockwell testers,
44
Vickers hardness number (HV)
conversions, 75-78
defined, 57-58
steel, approximate equivalent
hardness numbers, 154-155
table for, 59-62
Vickers hardness testers, 62-64
Vickers hardness testing, 57-65.
See also Vickers microhardness
testing.
equipment for, 58-65
indenters and indentations, and
Knoop, compared, 69-70
measuring indentation diagonals,
59
principles, 57-58
procedure, 64
Rockwell superficial hardness
tester for, 64-65
as static indentation test, 2, 58
surface conditions for, 145
testers for, 62-64
Vickers indenters, 68-70, 97
Vickers microhardness testing,
67-70, 97. See also Vickers hardness
testing.
Voids, in cemented carbides, 122
V scale (Rockwell), applications, 46,
125

W

Wear
of indenters, 27-28
rate, as hardness measure, 2
rate, for service life, 13
resistance, hardness evaluation by,
1, 12-13, 146
tests, 13-14

Wet-sand abrasion test, 14
Wire, microhardness testing, 68
Work hardening, and slip-line-field
theory, 11
Workpieces. See also Samples;
Specimen preparation; Surface
conditions; Surface(s).
circular, 25-26
cylindrical, 39, 50-51
for eddy current testing, 112
fixtures for, 74
flat, 49, 100-101
large, Rockwell tester for, 40-41
material, effect on test selection,
145-146
nonferrous metals, 124
nonstandard, Rockwell testing, 36,
37
for portable Brinell testers, 25-26
preparation and holding,
microhardness testing, 73-74
pyramidal Knoop indenter with
indentation in, 69
shape, and hardness test selection,
144
size, and hardness test selection,
143-144
size/shape, for Brinell testing, 29
small, microhardness testing, 68,
81-82
small, Model D Scleroscope for, 92
surface. See Surface conditions;
Surface(s).
thickness, for Rockwell testing,
47-49
thickness, in Brinell testing, 28
thin, durometer testing, 131
thin, microhardness testing, 68
in Vickers test, 64
Worm gear, Brinell testing machine,
22
W scale, Rockwell testing, 46n, 125n

X

X scale, Rockwell testing, 46n, 125n

Y

Yield point, high, 1
Y scale, Rockwell testing, 46n, 125n

Z

Zinc, hardness testing, 46, 125, 127